Numeracy

Revision for Adults
and Students

R Joinson

Sumbooks

First published in 1999 (MIM)

Sumbooks
Chester
CH4 8BB

Cover design: Abbie Joinson

ISBN 0 9531626 3 X

Printed in England by:
MFP Design & Print, Longford Trading Estate, Thomas Street, Stretford, Manchester, M30 0JT

Preface

This book is aimed at adults who have previously studied maths at school or college, but need to revise some or all of their basic numeracy. They range from those without any maths qualifications, to those who are well qualified.

There are many groups of people who might benefit, for example;

- Parents wanting to revise number work in order to help their children
- Returning students needing a basic knowledge of numeracy
- Those who lack confidence when dealing with numbers

The book can be used

- To dip into in order to look up a particular topic
- As a revision course, beginning at the front and working through it

The work is laid out so that one topic usually leads on to the next. Anyone feeling that they need to do the whole book is advised to begin with the easier topics at the front and work systematically to the end.

It is not intended for children to follow without the help of a teacher.

R Joinson   Chester 1999

Acknowledgements

I would like to thank Jenny, Sue, Hannah and Abbie who read the drafts and answered all the questions. Their suggestions were vital.

Contents

Saying and Writing Numbers

Saying numbers up to 999

For these numbers we have to say whether they are hundreds, tens or units.

<u>Units</u>: These are the numbers 1 to 9.
Just say the name of the number.
8 is said 'eight'.

<u>Tens</u>: In numbers from 10 to 99, there are two parts to say.
26 is 'twenty six'
78 is 'seventy eight'
90 is 'ninety'

<u>Hundreds</u>: In numbers from 100 to 999 we have to say three parts.
126 is 'one hundred and twenty six'
983 is 'nine hundred and eighty three'.
Where there are zeros, we don't say them.
700 is 'seven hundred'
708 is 'seven hundred and eight'
760 is 'seven hundred and sixty'.

Thousands

These are all the numbers between one thousand and nine hundred and ninety nine thousand.
They are 1,000 to 999,000
The numbers are grouped as 1, 2 or 3 digits to the left of the 3 lower numbers, usually with a comma or space between them.

1,000 is 'one thousand'
9,000 is 'nine thousand'
10,000 is 'ten thousand'
70,000 is 'seventy thousand'
300,000 is 'three hundred thousand'.

The comma or space is placed between the hundreds and the thousands in order to make them easier to read.

6,427 Six thousand four hundred and twenty seven (not six thousand <u>and</u> four hundred and twenty seven)
23 400 Twenty three thousand four hundred (not twenty three thousand <u>and</u> four hundred)
173,008 One hundred and seventy three thousand and eight
Remember not to say the zeros.
237 408 Two hundred and thirty seven thousand four hundred and eight.
983,500 Nine hundred and eighty three thousand five hundred.
714,041 Seven hundred and fourteen thousand and forty one.

Millions

The next three spaces to the left of the thousands are taken up by the millions.
1,000,000 One million
22,000,000 Twenty two million
346,000,000 Three hundred and forty six million
873,400,015 Eight hundred and seventy three million, four hundred thousand and fifteen.
Remember - get used to saying numbers in groups of three figures.

Billions

The next spaces to the left are taken up by billions.

1,000,000,000 is one billion
11,000,000,000 is eleven billion
and so on
Note. There are two definitions of a billion, the old British definition was one million million. However, the American and French definition, one thousand million, is now always used.

Remember

1 One has no zeros after it
10 Ten has one zero after the 1
100 One hundred has two zeros after the 1
1,000 One thousand has three zeros after the 1
10,000 Ten thousand has four zeros after the 1
100,000 One hundred thousand has five zeros after the 1
1,000,000 One million has six zeros after the 1
10,000,000 Ten million has seven zeros after the 1
100,000,000 One hundred million has eight zeros after the 1
1,000,000,000 One billion has nine zeros after the 1

Exercise 1

Write down these numbers in figures
Remember to put in the commas or spaces where necessary.
 1) Seventy six
 2) Three hundred and twenty seven
 3) Four hundred
 4) Eight hundred and fifty
 5) Nine hundred and six
 6) One thousand four hundred and thirty six
 7) Six thousand
 8) Eleven thousand four hundred
 9) Twenty seven thousand and sixty
 10) Seventy thousand and four
 11) One hundred and sixty three thousand nine hundred and fifty six
 12) Six hundred and seven thousand and eighty nine
 13) One million five hundred thousand
 14) Sixty three million four hundred and nine thousand six hundred and twenty eight
 15) One hundred and nine million and sixty three
 16) Three hundred and forty two million eight hundred and six thousand three hundred and twenty seven
 17) Seven billion
 18) Eight billion five hundred and six million
 19) One hundred billion

Exercise 2

Write down these numbers in words
 1) 79   2) 641
 3) 1314   4) 9302
 5) 18,004   6) 26,315
 7) 184,326   8) 940,521
 9) 600,000   10) 1,400,000
 11) 8,421,000 12) 27,000,314

Exercise 3

In each of the following pairs of numbers, say which is the bigger
1) 106 ; 160
2) 2,300 ; 3,200
3) 94,582 ; 100,000
4) 604,999 ; 640,000
5) 345,976 ; 346,000
6) 1,076,654 ; 10,000,000
7) 999,999 ; 900,000
8) 104,865 ; 140,865

The number system we use contains ten figures, 0, 1, 2, 3, 4, 5, 6, 7, 8 and 9.
When we count to values above 9, we use the same figures again; this time in pairs: 10, 11, 12 etc. When all the pairs are used up, we put three figures together and so on. 100 means ten tens or one hundred.
This systems of organising our numbers is called the Decimal System. Decimal because it has ten different figures in it. (From the Greek DEKA meaning 10 and the Latin DECI meaning one tenth).
The position of a figure in a number is very important. The position or places have names according to their value, like this:

Billions , Millions , Thousands , H T U
□□□   □□□   □□□   □□□

HTU means Hundreds, Tens and Units.

So   6 represents six units or 'six'
          60 represents six tens or 'sixty'
          600 represents six hundreds.
              Say 'six hundred'.
          6,000 represents six thousands.
              Say 'six thousand'
          60,000 represents six tens of thousands.
              Say 'sixty thousand'
          600,000 represents six hundreds of
              thousands.
              Say 'six hundred thousand'
6,000,000 represents six millions.
              Say 'six million'
                  and so on

If you consider the number 9348.
You will see that;
        the 8 has the value of 8 units
        the 4 has the value of 4 tens

the 3 has the value of 3 hundreds
and the 9 has the value of 9 thousands.

Notice that there are three places for the thousands.

Consider 436,000
        the 6 has the value of six thousands
        the 3 has the value of thirty thousands
and the 4 has the value of four hundred
        thousands.

Also there are three places for the millions.
In 532,000,000
        the 2 has the value of two millions
        the 3 has the value of thirty millions
and the 5 has the value of five hundred
        millions.

After millions, we get billions. One billion is one thousand million.
The number 5,000,000,000 is five billion.

Exercise
In each of the following questions, write down in words the value of the 6 each time.

1) 162	2) 386
3) 5463	4) 91, 642
5) 6,142	6) 4,623
7) 61,452	8) 261,315
9) 598,614	10) 415,621
11) 761,542	12) 816,714
13) 615,314	14) 683,812
15) 415,642	16) 562,415,815
17) 121,161,200	18) 6,421,502
19) 16,400,000	20) 816,834,184

Addition

To be able to do this you need to know what every pair of numbers from 1 to 9, add up to. These are called number pairs. i.e.

$$1 + 1 = 2$$
$$3 + 4 = 7$$
$$5 + 7 = 12$$
$$9 + 9 = 18$$
and so on.

By far the best way, and the classic way, to add is to put the numbers down underneath each other, in columns, according to the value of each figure.

Example 1
$$26 + 341$$
The 6 and the 1 are both valued in units so they should be in the same column (i.e. underneath each other). The 2 and 4 are both valued in tens so they should be in the same column.

So write down   2 6   Not   2 6
                 3 4 1   3 4 1

Begin to add up from the right hand column

Step 1   Step 2   Step 3
  2 6   2 6   2 6
3 4 1   3 4 1   3 4 1
    7   6 7   3 6 7

Exercise 1
In the same way as the example, add together each of these pairs of numbers.

1) 12 + 13   2) 123 + 45
3) 67 + 321   4) 73 + 324
5) 231 + 345   6) 724 + 145
7) 432 + 247   8) 593 + 202
9) 555 + 444   10) 372 + 517
11) 327 + 541   12) 654 + 234

Addition by carrying over

Example 2
$$247 + 326$$
Begin by adding together the 7 and the 6

H T U   Since the answer is 13, the
2 4 7   3 goes into the units column
3 2 6   and the 1 is carried over into
    3   the tens column.
  1

H T U   This 1 is then added on to
2 4 7   the 4 and 2 in the tens
3 2 6   column. Finally add
5 7 3   together the 3 and the 2.
  1

Example 3
$$257 + 595$$

2 5 7   Firstly add together the
5 9 5   7 and the 5.
    2
  1

2 5 7   Secondly add together the
5 9 5   5, 9 and 1.
  5 2
1 1

2 5 7   Thirdly add together the
5 9 5   2, 5 and 1.
8 5 2
1 1

Exercise 2
Add together each of the following pairs of numbers.

1) 247 + 382   2) 542 + 482
3) 562 + 257   4) 381 + 447
5) 662 + 247   6) 541 + 286
7) 435 + 215   8) 675 + 256
9) 342 + 587   10) 376 + 486
11) 483 + 433   12) 543 + 327
13) 537 + 389   14) 674 + 275

This idea can be extended to more numbers and larger numbers. Look at the next two examples:

Example 4

$$5{,}391 + 9{,}821$$

Step 1
```
  5 3 9 1
  9 8 2 1
        2
```

Step 2
```
  5 3 9 1
  9 8 2 1
      1 2
        1
```

Step 3
```
  5 3 9 1
  9 8 2 1
    2 1 2
    1 1
```

Step 4
```
  5 3 9 1
  9 8 2 1
1 5 2 1 2
    1 1
```

So $5{,}391 + 9{,}821 = 15{,}212$

Example 5

$$47 + 753 + 3494 + 764$$

Step 1
```
    4 7
  7 5 3
3 4 9 4
  7 6 4
      8
      1
```

Step 2
```
    4 7
  7 5 3
3 4 9 4
  7 6 4
    5 8
    2 1
```

Step 3
```
    4 7
  7 5 3
3 4 9 4
  7 6 4
  0 5 8
  2 2 1
```

Step 4
```
    4 7
  7 5 3
3 4 9 4
  7 6 4
5 0 5 8
  2 2 1
```

So $47 + 753 + 3{,}494 + 764 = 5{,}058$

Exercise 3
Add together the following sets of numbers

1) $57 + 86$
2) $341 + 599$
3) $762 + 838$
4) $1421 + 3842$
5) $3142 + 2157$
6) $10{,}321 + 1{,}482$
7) $27 + 38 + 542$
8) $263 + 542 + 387$
9) $36 + 842 + 1426$
10) $9541 + 162 + 76$
11) $1421 + 326 + 37 + 4287$
12) $8145 + 3142 + 27 + 641$

Now make up some more questions of your own. Check your answers by using a calculator.

Subtraction

There are at least two methods of subtraction. I will deal with both of them. If you have been taught subtraction and need to revise it, the best option is to keep with the system you know.

First you need to remember or be able to calculate quickly all the subtraction pairs up to 19.

$$19 - 1 = 18 \quad \text{and} \quad 19 - 18 = 1$$
$$19 - 2 = 17 \quad \text{and} \quad 19 - 17 = 2$$
$$19 - 3 = 16 \quad \text{and} \quad 19 - 16 = 3$$
$$19 - 4 = 15 \quad \text{and} \quad 19 - 15 = 4$$
etc.

$$8 - 1 = 7 \quad \text{and} \quad 8 - 7 = 1$$
$$8 - 2 = 6 \quad \text{and} \quad 8 - 6 = 2$$
$$8 - 3 = 5 \quad \text{and} \quad 8 - 5 = 3$$
$$8 - 4 = 4$$
etc

$$7 - 1 = 6 \quad \text{and} \quad 7 - 6 = 1$$
$$7 - 2 = 5 \quad \text{and} \quad 7 - 5 = 2$$
$$7 - 3 = 4 \quad \text{and} \quad 7 - 4 = 3$$

Try writing down some more yourself.

System 1 - Borrowing Method (Decomposition)

Note. Decomposition means to separate into its elements. In this method the first number is broken up although still retaining its value.

Example 1
$$22 - 6$$

$\begin{array}{r} 22 \\ -\ 6 \\ \hline \end{array}$ Change the 22 units into $10 + 12$ by 'borrowing' 1

This gives

$\begin{array}{r} {}^{1}\cancel{2}{}^{1}2 \\ -\ 6 \\ \hline \end{array}$

Subtracting the units gives

$\begin{array}{r} {}^{1}\cancel{2}{}^{1}2 \\ -\ 6 \\ \hline 6 \end{array}$

Subtracting the tens gives

$\begin{array}{r} {}^{1}\cancel{2}{}^{1}2 \\ -\ 06 \\ \hline 16 \end{array}$

So $22 - 6 = 16$

What have we done?
First, because we cannot do $2 - 6$ in the units column, we change the 22 into $10 + 12$. We have kept the total value of the number but written it down in a different way. Now we have $12 - 6$ which we can do.

Example 2
$$237 - 53$$

Subtracting the 3 from the 7 can be done straight away

$\begin{array}{r} 237 \\ -\ 53 \\ \hline 4 \end{array}$

Subtracting the 5 from the 3 cannot be done so we have to say $230 = 100 + 130$.

$\begin{array}{r} {}^{1}\cancel{2}37 \\ -\ 053 \\ \hline 4 \end{array}$

Now subtract the 5 from the 13 and 0 from the 1

$\begin{array}{r} {}^{1}\cancel{2}37 \\ -\ 053 \\ \hline 184 \end{array}$

Exercise 1
Use the method above to do these.

1) $14 - 7$ 2) $19 - 8$
3) $26 - 4$ 4) $37 - 9$
5) $53 - 6$ 6) $84 - 9$
7) $27 - 16$ 8) $36 - 19$

9) 83 – 37   10) 135 – 29
11) 256 – 142   12) 364 – 143
13) 362 – 248   14) 356 – 128
15) 284 – 125   16) 387 – 159
17) 756 – 427   18) 842 – 629
19) 3482 – 2146   20) 5753 – 3147

Example 3
$$437 – 381$$

Firstly subtract the   4 3 7
1 from the 7 $-$3 8 1
                         ‾‾‾‾‾‾‾6

Since 8 cannot be   ³4¹3 7
taken from 3 we must $-$3 8 1
borrow from the 4   ‾‾‾‾0 5 6

So 437 – 381 = 56

Note
437 on the top line has been changed to
300 + 13 (tens) + 7
or 300 + 130 + 7

Exercise 2
1) 347 – 54   2) 453 – 91
3) 641 – 150   4) 453 – 292
5) 867 – 393   6) 547 – 256
7) 543 – 292   8) 654 – 372

Example 4
$$147 – 58$$
Here we have to borrow twice

Borrow from the 4   1³4¹7
                         $-$ 5 8
                         ‾‾‾‾‾‾‾9

Borrow from the 1   ⁰1³4¹7
                         $-$ 5 8
                         ‾‾‾‾0 8 9

So 147 – 58 = 89

Exercise 3
1) 243 – 67   2) 542 – 77
3) 381 – 93   4) 227 – 69
5) 315 – 138   6) 427 – 339
7) 426 – 289   8) 432 – 257

Sometimes we don't have anything to
borrow from.

Example 5
$$504 – 9$$
Because we cannot take 9 from 4 we must
borrow. But since there is nothing we can
borrow from the tens position, we must
borrow from the hundreds position. So
500 becomes 400 + 10 (tens)

Now we can borrow   ⁴5¹04
from the tens position. $-$ 9
                          ‾‾‾‾‾‾

Change the top line   ⁴5⁹¹04
to 400 + 9 (tens) + 14 $-$ 9
= 400 + 90 + 14 = 504   ‾‾‾4 9 5

So 504 – 9 = 495

Where we have to borrow from zeros, we
move along to the next position until we
can borrow, then move back.

  5 0 0   ⁴5¹0 0   ⁴5⁹¹0⁰0
$-$5 3   ⟶ $-$5 3   ⟶ $-$ 5 3
‾‾‾‾‾   ‾‾‾‾‾   ‾‾‾4 4 7

So 500 – 53 = 447

Exercise 4
1) 304 – 7   2) 805 – 17
3) 603 – 28   4) 900 – 32
5) 500 – 43   6) 700 – 152
7) 600 – 190   8) 308 – 197
9) 500 – 273   10) 1000 – 174
11) 2000 – 1342   12) 8000 – 3426

Now set yourself some more questions and
use your calculator to check them.

System 2 - Paying back Method
(Equal addition)

Look at this.

$6 - 2 = 4$
$16 - 12 = 4$

$37 - 22 = 15$
$47 - 32 = 15$

If the same number is added to both the numbers in a subtraction, then the answer will be the same.
This is the basis of the Equal Addition method of subtraction.

Example 6
$$22 - 6$$

$$\begin{array}{r} 22 \\ -\ 6 \\ \hline \end{array}$$

Add 10 to the units column in the top line and 10 to the tens column in the second line.

$$\begin{array}{r} 2\overset{1}{2} \\ -_16 \\ \hline 16 \end{array}$$

Subtract the 6 from the 12 and the 1 from the 2

10 has been added to both the top and bottom numbers.
The top line has become $20 + 12 = 32$
The bottom line has become $10 + 6 = 16$
This gives $32 - 16$, which gets the same answer as the original question of $22 - 6$.
i.e.
$22 - 6$ is the same as $32 - 16$

Example 7
$$237 - 53$$
Subtracting the 3 from the 7 can be done straight away

$$\begin{array}{r} 237 \\ -\ 53 \\ \hline 4 \end{array}$$

Now add 100 to both the lines.
The top line now becomes $200 + 130 + 7$ and the bottom line becomes $100 + 50 + 3$.

$$\begin{array}{r} 2\overset{1}{3}7 \\ -_153 \\ \hline 4 \end{array}$$

Finally subtract 5 from 13 and 1 from 2.

$$\begin{array}{r} 2\overset{1}{3}7 \\ -_153 \\ \hline 184 \end{array}$$

Exercise 5
Do all the questions from exercise 1.

Example 8
$$437 - 381$$

Firstly subtract the 1 from the 7.

$$\begin{array}{r} 437 \\ -381 \\ \hline 6 \end{array}$$

Since 8 cannot be taken from 3 we must add 100 to both the top and the bottom. Now subtract the 8 from the 13 and the 4 from the 4.

$$\begin{array}{r} 4\overset{1}{3}7 \\ -_4381 \\ \hline 056 \end{array}$$

So $437 - 381 = 56$

Exercise 6
Do all the questions from exercise 2.

Example 9
$$147 - 58$$
Here we have to add 10 and then 100 to the top and bottom lines.

First add 10 to top and bottom then subtract the 8 from 17.

$$\begin{array}{r} 14\overset{1}{7} \\ -_658 \\ \hline 9 \end{array}$$

Finally add 100 to top and bottom, then subtract the 6 from the 14 and the 1 from 1.

$$\begin{array}{r} 1\overset{1}{4}\overset{1}{7} \\ -_158 \\ \hline 089 \end{array}$$

So $147 - 58 = 89$

Exercise 7
Do all the questions from exercise 3

Exercise 8
Do all the questions from exercise 4

Multiplication Tables

It is very useful to remember your tables. However, some people find them quite difficult, particularly the middle numbers ($7 \times 8 = 56$, $9 \times 6 = 54$ etc). Here are the tables with helpful hints. It is only necessary to remember up to 9×9.

2 Times	3 Times
$1 \times 2 = 2$	$1 \times 3 = 3$
$2 \times 2 = 4$	$2 \times 3 = 6$
$3 \times 2 = 6$	$3 \times 3 = 9$
$4 \times 2 = 8$	$4 \times 3 = 12$
$5 \times 2 = 10$	$5 \times 3 = 15$
$6 \times 2 = 12$	$6 \times 3 = 18$
$7 \times 2 = 14$	$7 \times 3 = 21$
$8 \times 2 = 16$	$8 \times 3 = 24$
$9 \times 2 = 18$	$9 \times 3 = 27$
All even numbers	

4 Times	5 Times
$1 \times 4 = 4$	$1 \times 5 = 5$
$2 \times 4 = 8$	$2 \times 5 = 10$
$3 \times 4 = 12$	$3 \times 5 = 15$
$4 \times 4 = 16$	$4 \times 5 = 20$
$5 \times 4 = 20$	$5 \times 5 = 25$
$6 \times 4 = 24$	$6 \times 5 = 30$
$7 \times 4 = 28$	$7 \times 5 = 35$
$8 \times 4 = 32$	$8 \times 5 = 40$
$9 \times 4 = 36$	$9 \times 5 = 45$
All even numbers	All end in 5 or 0

6 Times	7 Times
$1 \times 6 = 6$	$1 \times 7 = 7$
$2 \times 6 = 12$	$2 \times 7 = 14$
$3 \times 6 = 18$	$3 \times 7 = 21$
$4 \times 6 = 24$	$4 \times 7 = 28$
$5 \times 6 = 30$	$5 \times 7 = 35$
$6 \times 6 = 36$	$6 \times 7 = 42$
$7 \times 6 = 42$	$7 \times 7 = 49$
$8 \times 6 = 48$	$8 \times 7 = 56$
$9 \times 6 = 54$	$9 \times 7 = 63$
All even numbers	

8 Times	9 Times
$1 \times 8 = 8$	$1 \times 9 = 9$
$2 \times 8 = 16$	$2 \times 9 = 18$
$3 \times 8 = 24$	$3 \times 9 = 27$
$4 \times 8 = 32$	$4 \times 9 = 36$
$5 \times 8 = 40$	$5 \times 9 = 45$
$6 \times 8 = 48$	$6 \times 9 = 54$
$7 \times 8 = 56$	$7 \times 9 = 63$
$8 \times 8 = 64$	$8 \times 9 = 72$
$9 \times 8 = 72$	$9 \times 9 = 81$
All even numbers	

(Note that an even number is one divisable by 2. An odd number is any other number)

Helpful Hints

1. If you can't remember the multiplication one way round, you may remember it the other way.
   ie. $3 \times 5 = 15$ and $5 \times 3 = 15$
   $7 \times 8 = 56$ and $8 \times 7 = 56$

2. When you multiply by an even number, you always get an even number as an answer.
   ie. $3 \times 2 = 6$ $8 \times 3 = 24$ $4 \times 4 = 16$

3. Only when two odd numbers are multiplied together do you get an odd number answer.
   ie. $3 \times 3 = 9$ $5 \times 7 = 35$ etc.

4. In the 9 times tables, the figures in the answers always add up to 9.
   ie. $1 + 8 = 9$ $2 + 7 = 9$ $3 + 6 = 9$

5. In the 5 times tables, all the answers end in 5 or 0.

6. If you can't remember, try doubling up.
   ie. $3 \times 7 = 21$ so $6 \times 7 = 42$
   $4 \times 8 = 32$ so $8 \times 8 = 64$
   $2 \times 7 = 14$ so $4 \times 7 = 28$
   and $8 \times 7 = 56$

Number Patterns

The multiplication tables are examples of number patterns.

Example 1

Consider the two times table

2, 4, 6, 8, 10, 12, 14...

these numbers increase by 2 each time. We can look at this pattern and predict that the next number in the pattern is 16.

Example 2

Similarly with the 5 times tables

5, 10, 15, 20, 25, 30, 35...

these numbers increase by 5 each time. We can predict that the next number in the pattern is 40.

Sometimes the numbers increase by the same amount but don't follow a particular times table.

Example 3

7, 12, 17, 22, 27, 32...

In this case the numbers increase by 5 but begin with 7 and not 5. The next number in the pattern is 32 + 5 = 37

Exercise 1

In each of the following number patterns, write down the next three numbers.

1) 7, 14, 21, 28, 35...
2) 9, 18, 27, 36, 45...
3) 5, 9, 13, 17, 21...
4) 5, 7, 9, 11, 13...
5) 7, 10, 13, 16, 19...
6) 3, 8, 13, 18, 23...
7) 3, 12, 21, 30, 39...

Sometimes the numbers don't increase by the same amount, but the increase itself increases

Example 4

1, 2, 4, 7, 11, 16...

These numbers increase by 1, 2, 3, 4, 5...

i.e 1 + 1 = 2

2 + 2 = 4

4 + 3 = 7

7 + 4 = 11

11 + 5 = 16

so the next number will be 16 + 6 = 22, then 22 + 7 = 29, then 29 + 8 = 37 and so on.

Exercise 2

In each of the following number patterns write down the next three numbers.

1) 3, 4, 6, 9, 13...
2) 5, 5, 6, 8, 11...
3) 5, 7, 11, 17, 25...
4) 2, 3, 5, 8, 12...
5) 20, 21, 23, 26, 30...
6) 3, 5, 8, 12, 17...
7) 9, 11, 15, 21, 29...

Sometimes the number pattern decreases

Example 5

45, 40, 35, 30...

these numbers are decreasing in steps of 5. The next numbers are 25, 20 and 15

Example 6

45, 44, 42, 39, 35...

these numbers decrease by 1, 2, 3, 4 and so on. The next numbers will be

35 − 5 = 30

30 − 6 = 24

and 24 − 7 = 17

Exercise 3

In each of the following number patterns, write down the next three numbers.

1) 25, 23, 21, 19, 17...
2) 36, 32, 28, 24, 20...
3) 55, 51, 47, 43, 39...
4) 42, 39, 36, 33, 30...
5) 35, 33, 30, 26, 21...
6) 67, 65, 61, 55, 47...
7) 75, 70, 64, 57, 49...

Multiplication

For multiplying numbers ending with zeros, see page 21

Multiplying a 2 figure number by a 1 figure number

Example 1

Without carrying over

```
  3 2
× 3
 9 6
```

Example 2

With carrying over

```
  4 5
× 7
3 1 5
  3
```

Note

$7 \times 5 = 35$. This means 3 tens + 5 units. Put the 5 units in the units column and carry over the 3 tens to the tens column. Finally, $7 \times 4 = 28$, then add on the 3 to give 31.

Exercise 1

1) 21×4 2) 43×2
3) 33×3 4) 17×5
5) 26×7 6) 37×4
7) 43×6 8) 84×5
9) 96×4 10) 89×8

Multiplying a 2 figure number by a 2 figure number

Example 2

27×34

```
  2   Put the carry over numbers
  2        up here
  2 7
× 3 4
1 0 8    (this is 27 × 4)
+8 1 0    (this is 27 × 30)
9 1 8
```

Firstly $4 \times 7 = 28$. Put the 8 down underneath the 4 and carry over the 2 into the tens column. Next, $4 \times 2 = 8$. This goes underneath the 3

but first add on the 2 which you carried over, to get 10.

Now you have to multiply by the 3 (or 30) $3 \times 7 = 21$. Put the 1 down underneath the 3 and carry over the 2. Put a 0 to the right of the 1 because you have multiplied by 30 and not 3.

Next $3 \times 2 = 6$ and add on the second 2 you carried over. Put down the 8 under the 1. Finally add together the two lines to get 918.

Exercise 2

1) 22×14 2) 43×32
3) 53×17 4) 48×29
5) 53×32 6) 64×42
7) 13×42 8) 87×52
9) 91×36 10) 95×64

Multiplying a 3 figure number by a 2 figure number

Example 3

132×57

```
  1 1
  2 1
  1 3 2
×   5 7
  9 2 4    (132 × 7)
6 6 0 0    (132 × 50)
7 5 2 4
    1
```

Exercise 3

1) 106×17 2) 231×21
3) 297×32 4) 341×38
5) 476×46 6) 552×35
7) 647×28 8) 752×51
9) 872×63 10) 981×87

Now set yourself some more questions and use your calculator to check them.

Short Division (Share)

Division can be carried out as short division or long division. Short division is used when the number we are dividing by has just one figure, such as $853 \div 6$. Long division is carried out when the number we are dividing by has more than one figure, such as $853 \div 16$.

Short Division

Example 1
$$741 \div 3$$

Step 1

$$3\overline{)7\,{}^14\,1}$$ with a 2 on top

3 goes into 7 twice with 1 remaining. Carry over the 1

Step 2

$$3\overline{)7\,{}^14\,{}^21}$$ with 24 on top

3 goes into 14, 4 times with 2 remaining. Carry over the 2.

Step 3

$$3\overline{)7\,{}^14\,{}^21}$$ with 247 on top

3 goes into 21 exactly 7 times without any remainder.

So $741 \div 3 = 247$

Example 2
$$842 \div 7$$

Step 1

$$7\overline{)8\,{}^14\,2}$$ with 1 on top

7 goes into 8 once with 1 remaining.

Step 2

$$7\overline{)8\,{}^14\,2}$$ with 12 on top

7 goes into 14 twice exactly.

Step 3

$$7\overline{)8\,{}^14\,2}$$ with 120 r2 on top

7 goes into 2 zero times with 2 remaining.

So $842 \div 7 = 120$ with a remainder of 2.

Notice step 3
Don't say 7 won't go into 2 and then ignore it. Say 7 goes into 2 zero times with a remainder of 2. This will always remind you to do it properly.

Example 3
$$273 \div 4$$

Step 1

$$4\overline{)2\,{}^27\,3}$$ with 0 on top

4 goes into 2 zero times with 2 remaining

Step 2

$$4\overline{)2\,{}^27\,{}^33}$$ with 06 on top

4 goes into 27 six times with 3 remaining

Step 3

$$4\overline{)2\,{}^27\,{}^33}$$ with 068 r1 on top

4 goes into 33 eight times with 1 remaining

Exercise
1) $132 \div 3$	2) $284 \div 4$
3) $536 \div 6$	4) $342 \div 7$
5) $486 \div 5$	6) $861 \div 8$
7) $794 \div 2$	8) $356 \div 9$
9) $542 \div 6$	10) $868 \div 5$
11) $654 \div 7$	12) $927 \div 4$
13) $587 \div 8$	14) $765 \div 6$

This is done when the number we are dividing by has two or more figures in it.

Method 1
Continuous Subtraction
Example 1

$$893 \div 17$$

```
 893
-170   10    (10 × 17 = 170)
 723
-170   10
 553
-170   10
 383
-170   10
 213
-170   10
  43
 -17    1    (1 × 17 = 17)
  26
 -17    1
   9   52
   ↑   ↑↑
```

Remainder   Add together this column. This gives the number of 17's in 893.

First subtract 170 as this is 17×10 and easy to remember. Then subtract 170 again and continue doing this until you cannot subtract 170 any longer. At that point subtract 17's until there is a remainder of less than 17.

So $893 \div 17 = 52$ remainder 9

Method 2
Example 2

$$893 \div 17$$

Step 1

```
       5
  17)8 9 3
     8 5
```

calculations

```
  1 7/        1 7
  ×4/         × 5
  68          8 5
```
First try   Second try

First calculate the number of times 17 divides into 89. You might need to do a few multiplications before getting the answer. Put the results into the division and subtract to find the remainder then bring down the 3.

Step 2

```
        5
  17)8 9 3
     8 5
     4 3
```
Subtract the 85 from the 89. Bring down the 3. Now divide 43 by 17.

Step 3

```
       5 2
  17)8 9 3
    -8 5  ——— 17 × 5 = 85
     4 3
    -3 4  ——— 17 × 2 = 34
       9  ——— remainder
```

So $893 \div 17 = 52$ remainder 9

Exercise
Calculate these using either of the above methods.

1) $168 \div 14$	2) $137 \div 11$
3) $238 \div 17$	4) $330 \div 22$
5) $342 \div 15$	6) $555 \div 15$
7) $481 \div 14$	8) $834 \div 16$
9) $786 \div 27$	10) $1224 \div 24$
11) $652 \div 43$	12) $1391 \div 13$
13) $942 \div 43$	14) $1548 \div 43$
15) $842 \div 27$	16) $1071 \div 17$
17) $981 \div 42$	18) $2368 \div 64$
19) $1322 \div 57$	20) $2440 \div 76$
21) $3421 \div 72$	22) $2304 \div 36$
23) $2384 \div 57$	24) $2907 \div 19$

Rounding off and Estimating

Sometimes it is not necessary to get the correct answer to a problem and an estimate will do.

Example 1
We could say that 48 is about 50 or that 137 is nearly 140. These numbers have been rounded off to the nearest 10. Here are some examples of numbers rounded off to the nearest 10.

57 60
134 130
208 210
541 540
85 90

(85 could be rounded up to make 90 or rounded down to make 80 because it is exactly halfway between 80 and 90. The convention is to round up, for good mathematical reasons. In this book I will always round up)

Exercise 1
Round off these numbers to the nearest 10.

1) 73   2) 87   3) 142   4) 251
5) 175   6) 174   7) 352   8) 547
9) 683   10) 756 11) 876   12) 947

Rounding off to other numbers
Example 2
These numbers have been rounded off to the nearest 100.

175 200
452 500
683 700
824 800
1243 1200

7542 7500
9679 9700

These numbers have been rounded off to the nearest thousand.

3485 3000
5784 6000
7500 8000   (rounded up to 8000 rather
25,451 25,000   than down to 7000)
17,722 18,000

Exercise 2
Round off each of these numbers in the way indicated in the brackets.

1) 27   (nearest 10)   2) 4900   (1000)
3) 614   (100)   4) 3100   (1000)
5) 347   (100)   6) 172   (10)
7) 475   (10)   8) 143   (10)
9) 6741   (1000)   10) 851   (100)
11) 5422   (1000)   12) 1370   (100)
13) 6482   (1000)   14) 97   (10)
15) 3422   (100)   16) 1251   (100)
17) 8742   (1000)   18) 5472   (1000)
19) 186   (10)   20) 17,694 (1000)
21) 351   (10)   22) 36,421 (1000)
23) 5976   (100)   24) 4392   (1000)
25) 399   (10)   26) 247   (10)
27) 8427   (100)   28) 11,223 (10)
29) 11, 223 (100)   30) 11,223 (1000)
31) The attendance at a football match was
    23,251. Write down this value;
a) correct to the nearest thousand
b) correct to the nearest hundred
c) correct to the nearest 10

Multiplying Numbers Ending in Zeros

Multiplying by 10, 100, 1000 etc

The quick way to multiply by 10 is to put a zero on the end.

$$2 \times 10 = 20$$
$$14 \times 10 = 140$$
$$176 \times 10 = 1760$$
and so on

Multiplying by 100 can be done similarly. This time two zeros are put on the end.

$$3 \times 100 = 300$$
$$27 \times 100 = 2700$$
$$156 \times 100 = 15600$$
and so on

So there is a simple rule when multiplying whole numbers by 10, 100, 1000 etc. Just write down the number of zeros at the end of the number.

$$5 \times 100 = 500$$
$$16 \times 10 = 160$$
$$257 \times 100 = 25700$$
and so on

Exercise 1

Write down the answers to these multiplications.

1) 8×10
2) 9×100
3) 20×100
4) 61×1000
5) 27×10
6) 340×100
7) 86×1000
8) 9×10000
9) 4314×10
10) 784×100
11) 953×10
12) 864×1000

Multiplying numbers containing 1 figure and zeros

Examples

We know that $3 \times 2 = 6$

so $30 \times 2 = 60$

(because 30 is 10 times bigger than 3, then the answer must be 10 times bigger than 6)

Similarly since $300 \times 2 = 600$
$$3000 \times 2 = 6000$$
$$30,000 \times 2 = 60,000$$
and so on

Also since $3 \times 2 = 6$
$$3 \times 20 = 60$$
$$3 \times 200 = 600$$
$$3 \times 2000 = 6000$$
$$3 \times 20,000 = 60,000$$
and so on

and since $3 \times 2 = 6$

$30 \times 2 = 60$ 1 zero in the answer
$30 \times 20 = 600$ 2 zeros in the answer
$300 \times 20 = 6000$ 3 zeros in the answer
$300 \times 200 = 60,000$ 4 0's in the answer
$3000 \times 200 = 600,000$ 5 0's in the answer
and so on.

Rule. When multiplying numbers where there is one figure with zeros at the end of the number, multiply the figures together and put all the zeros on the end.

$$40 \times 20 = 800$$
$$\uparrow \quad \uparrow \quad \uparrow\uparrow$$
2 zeros   2 zeros

$$500 \times 300 = 150,000$$
$$\uparrow\uparrow \quad \uparrow\uparrow \quad \uparrow\uparrow\uparrow\uparrow$$
4 zeros   4 zeros

Exercise 2

Write down the answers to these

1) 50×6
2) 2×200
3) 50×7
4) 40×80
5) 90×20
6) 200×30
7) 500×200
8) 600×70
9) 600×200
10) 3000×30
11) 7000×200
12) 600×7000
13) 6000×2000
14) 7000×5000
15) 6000×8000
16) $700,000 \times 200$

Recap Test 1 - Numbers

1) Write down these numbers in figures.
a) One hundred and sixty seven.
b) Sixteen thousand four hundred.
c) One hundred and fifty six thousand, three hundred and forty three.
d) Six million and six.

2) Write down these numbers in words.
a) 68   b) 157   c) 7482   d) 12,421
e) 256,421   f) 3,000,000
g) 5,400,000   h) 16,254,000

3) Which number in the following pairs is the bigger?
a) 250 ; 205   b) 100,000 ; 96,000
c) 3,400 ; 5,000   d) 852,500 ; 654,329

4) In each of the following numbers, say what the value of the 5 is each time (i.e. units, tens, hundreds etc)
a) 547   b) 3425   c) 27452
d) 125,426   e) 5,126,424   f) 6,534,321

5) Write down the following numbers in order of size, smallest first.
9142 ;   572 ;   1432 ;   27 ;   81,562 ;
684 ;   500 ;   8 million ;   934,381

6) In the following additions show all your calculation
a) 52 + 47   b) 189 + 69   c) 1254 + 956
d) 27 + 841 + 3142
e) 1426 + 2345 + 98 + 63

7) In the following subtractions, show all your calculations.
a) 37 – 14   b) 83 – 69   c) 284 – 39
d) 541 – 397   e) 2000 – 1159

8) Times tables - use your memory to write down the answers to the following multiplications.

a) 2×9 b) 4×6 c) 5×7
d) 6×8 e) 7×8 f) 9×6
g) 9×7 h) 9×9 i) 8×9

9) Write down the next 3 numbers in each of these patterns.
a) 6, 12, 18, 24, 30...
b) 40, 38, 36, 34, 32...
c) 5, 7, 10, 14, 19...
d) 81, 78, 73, 66, 57...

10) Showing all your calculations, do these multiplications.
a) 27×2 b) 47×33 c) 324×36

11) Showing all your calculations, do these divisions.
a) $437 \div 3$ b) $743 \div 7$ c) $564 \div 15$
d) $3246 \div 43$

12) Round off each of the following numbers in the way indicated
a) 73 to the nearest 10
b) 87 to the nearest 10
c) 684 to the nearest 100
d) 1482 to the nearest 100
e) 12,423 to the nearest 100
f) 647 to the nearest 10

13) Write down the answers to these multiplications without doing any written calculations.
a) 40×3 b) 50×30 c) 400×20
d) 5000×6 e) 6000×70
f) $50,000 \times 300$ g) $200,000 \times 6$
h) $50,000 \times 3000$

Definition of a Fraction

A fraction of something is a part of it. Whenever something is broken up into smaller parts, these parts are called fractions.

Examples
Read carefully through each of these examples. When you understand them do the exercise.

Example 1

4 equal parts altogether, 1 part shaded in.

The shaded in part is $\frac{1}{4}$ (one quarter) of the whole square

Example 2

3 equal parts altogether, 1 part shaded in.

The shaded part is $\frac{1}{3}$ (one third) of the whole triangle.

Example 3

$\frac{1}{2}$ (half) is shaded in.

Example 4

$\frac{1}{8}$ (one eighth) is shaded in.

Example 5

$\frac{1}{6}$ (one sixth) is shaded in.

Example 6

3 parts out of 4 are shaded
$\frac{3}{4}$ (three quarters) of the square is shaded in.

Example 7

7 parts out of 8 are shaded.
$\frac{7}{8}$ (seven eighths) of the rectangle are shaded in.
$\frac{1}{8}$ (one eighth) of the rectangle is not shaded in.

Example 8
5 circles out of 9 circles are black.
$\frac{5}{9}$ (five ninths) are black.
$\frac{4}{9}$ (four ninths) are white.

Example 9

$\frac{5}{8}$ (five eighths) of the strip are shaded.
$\frac{3}{8}$ (three eighths) of the strip are unshaded.

Example 10
There are 12 people working in an office. 7 are men and 5 are women.
$\frac{7}{12}$ of the office workers are men.
$\frac{5}{12}$ of the office workers are women.

Example 11
A box contains 21 snooker balls. Fifteen of the balls are red.
$\frac{15}{21}$ of the balls are red.
$\frac{6}{21}$ of the balls are not red.

Exercise
1)
a) What fraction is shaded in?
b) What fraction is unshaded?

23

2) ○ ● ○ ● ○   a) What fraction is black?
   ● ○ ● ○ ●
   ○ ● ○ ● ○   b) What fraction is white?

3)

   a) What fraction is shaded in?
   b) What fraction is unshaded?

4) 25 students sit an examination.
   17 pass and the remainder fail.
   a) What fraction of the students pass?
   b) What fraction of the students fail?

5) Gary walks from his home to the centre of town, a distance of 7 miles. When he has walked 4 miles he stops for a rest.
   a) What fraction of the journey has he travelled when he stops?
   b) What fraction of the journey has he got left?

6) ABRACADABRA
   a) What fraction of this word is made up of A's?
   b) What fraction of this word is made up of B's?
   c) What fraction of this word is made up of C's?
   d) What fraction of this word is made up of D's?
   e) What fraction of this word is made up of R's?

7) A bunch of flowers is made up of 9 yellow roses, 5 red roses and 3 white roses
   a) What fraction of the bunch are yellow roses?
   b) What fraction of the bunch are red roses?
   c) What fraction of the bunch are white roses?

$\frac{1}{2}$ (cut into 2 equal parts)

$\frac{1}{4}$ (cut into 4 equal parts)

$\frac{1}{8}$ (cut into 8 equal parts)

$\frac{1}{16}$ (cut into 16 equal parts)

$\frac{1}{2}$ is bigger than $\frac{1}{4}$

$\frac{1}{4}$ is bigger than $\frac{1}{8}$

$\frac{1}{8}$ is bigger than $\frac{1}{16}$

The larger the number on the bottom, the smaller is the value of the fraction.

Exercise 1

1) Is $\frac{1}{16}$ bigger than $\frac{1}{8}$?

2) Is $\frac{1}{8}$ smaller than $\frac{1}{4}$?

3) Which is the smaller, $\frac{1}{4}$ or $\frac{1}{8}$?

In questions 4 to 6 use the diagrams above

to help you.

4) How many $\frac{1}{4}$'s make $\frac{1}{2}$?

5) How many $\frac{1}{8}$'s make $\frac{1}{4}$?

6) How many $\frac{1}{8}$'s make $\frac{1}{2}$?

7) Write down these fractions in order of size, smallest to largest.

$$\frac{1}{3}, \frac{1}{8}, \frac{1}{4}, \frac{1}{2}, \frac{1}{5}, \frac{1}{7}, \frac{1}{12}.$$

Finding parts of numbers 1

Example 1

To find half of something, divide by 2.

$$\frac{1}{2} \text{ of 16 is } 16 \div 2 = 8.$$

Example 2

To find $\frac{1}{3}$ of something, divide by 3.

$$\frac{1}{3} \text{ of 15 is } 15 \div 3 = 5.$$

Example 3

To find $\frac{1}{6}$ of something, divide by 6.

$$\frac{1}{6} \text{ of 24 is } 24 \div 6 = 4.$$

Exercise 2

Work out these.

1) $\frac{1}{2}$ of 20

2) $\frac{1}{2}$ of 10

3) $\frac{1}{3}$ of 9

4) $\frac{1}{3}$ of 21

5) $\frac{1}{6}$ of 30

6) $\frac{1}{6}$ of 36

7) $\frac{1}{4}$ of 20

8) $\frac{1}{4}$ of 40

9) $\frac{1}{5}$ of 15

10) $\frac{1}{5}$ of 25

11) $\frac{1}{10}$ of 40

12) $\frac{1}{10}$ of 80

13) $\frac{1}{2}$ of 16 apples

14) $\frac{1}{3}$ of 30 cm.

15) $\frac{1}{4}$ of 24 hours

16) $\frac{1}{5}$ of 30 cakes

17) $\frac{1}{10}$ of 20 days

18) $\frac{1}{3}$ of 18 loaves

19) $\frac{1}{4}$ of 40 mm.

20) $\frac{1}{5}$ of 25 oranges

Adding Fractions

Example 4

$$\frac{1}{5} + \frac{1}{5} = \frac{2}{5}$$

Example 5

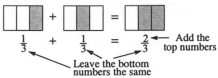

$\frac{1}{3} + \frac{1}{3} = \frac{2}{3}$ ← Add the top numbers

Leave the bottom numbers the same

Example 6

$\frac{1}{7} + \frac{1}{7} = \frac{2}{7}$

Example 7

$\frac{2}{7} + \frac{1}{7} = \frac{3}{7}$

Example 8

$\frac{4}{10} + \frac{5}{10} = \frac{9}{10}$

---

3 —— This is called the **numerator**
5 —— This is called the **denominator**
The denominator tells us the *type* of fraction and the numerator tells us *how many* there are.

Exercise 3

Add these together

1) $\frac{3}{5} + \frac{1}{5}$ 2) $\frac{4}{10} + \frac{3}{10}$

3) $\frac{2}{7} + \frac{3}{7}$ 4) $\frac{3}{8} + \frac{2}{8}$

5) $\frac{1}{5} + \frac{2}{5}$ 6) $\frac{2}{6} + \frac{3}{6}$

7) $\frac{2}{9} + \frac{3}{9}$ 8) $\frac{3}{16} + \frac{8}{16}$

9) $\frac{3}{20} + \frac{6}{20}$ 10) $\frac{5}{12} + \frac{2}{12}$

11) $\frac{3}{18} + \frac{8}{18}$ 12) $\frac{9}{20} + \frac{2}{20}$

Finding parts of numbers 2

Example 9

To find $\frac{2}{3}$ of 15

$\frac{1}{3}$ of 15 is $15 \div 3 = 5$

So $\frac{2}{3}$ of 15 is twice one third or $5 \times 2 = 10$

To find a fraction of a number, divide by the denominator and multiply by the numerator.

Example 10

To find $\frac{3}{4}$ of 20

$\frac{1}{4}$ of 20 is $20 \div 4 = 5$

So $\frac{3}{4}$ of 20 is $5 \times 3 = 15$

Example 12

To find $\frac{5}{8}$ of 24

$\frac{1}{8}$ of 24 is $24 \div 8 = 3$

So $\frac{5}{8}$ of 24 is $3 \times 5 = 15$

Exercise 4

Calculate these

1) $\frac{2}{5}$ of 20   2) $\frac{3}{5}$ of 25

3) $\frac{3}{8}$ of 24   4) $\frac{3}{7}$ of 21

5) $\frac{5}{6}$ of 18   6) $\frac{3}{4}$ of 20

7) $\frac{5}{7}$ of 28   8) $\frac{7}{10}$ of 30

9) $\frac{5}{8}$ of 32   10) $\frac{3}{10}$ of 40

11) $\frac{9}{10}$ of 50   12) $\frac{3}{12}$ of 60

13) $\frac{3}{4}$ of 40 apples   14) $\frac{3}{5}$ of 35 cakes

15) $\frac{2}{3}$ of 21 days   16) $\frac{5}{8}$ of 40 mm.

17) $\frac{4}{5}$ of £60   18) $\frac{7}{8}$ of 64 metres

Equivalent Fraction

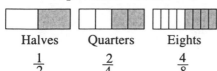

Halves   Quarters   Eights

$\frac{1}{2}$ $\frac{2}{4}$ $\frac{4}{8}$

In each large rectangle, $\frac{1}{2}$ of it has been shaded in.

So $\frac{1}{2} = \frac{2}{4}$

and $\frac{1}{2} = \frac{4}{8}$

and so on.

Similarly

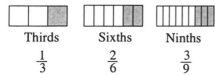

Thirds   Sixths   Ninths

$\frac{1}{3}$ $\frac{2}{6}$ $\frac{3}{9}$

In each large rectangle, $\frac{1}{3}$ of it has been shaded in.

So $\frac{1}{3} = \frac{2}{6}$

and $\frac{1}{3} = \frac{3}{9}$

and so on.

These fractions are called 'equivalent fractions'.

When we talk about a fraction we always think of the fraction with the lowest numbers in it.

 We call this $\frac{1}{2}$ not $\frac{2}{4}$

To change fractions into their lowest terms divide the numerator and denominator by another (same) number.

$$\frac{4 \div 4}{8 \div 4} = \frac{1}{2}$$

$$\frac{6 \div 6}{12 \div 6} = \frac{1}{2}$$

$$\frac{5 \div 5}{15 \div 5} = \frac{1}{3}$$

$$\frac{6 \div 3}{9 \div 3} = \frac{2}{3}$$

and so on

This is known as 'cancelling down'

Exercise

Put these fractions into their lowest terms by dividing the numerator and the denominator by the same number (cancelling down).

1) $\frac{5}{20}$ 2) $\frac{4}{20}$ 3) $\frac{4}{16}$

4) $\frac{3}{15}$ 5) $\frac{2}{6}$ 6) $\frac{4}{12}$

7) $\frac{6}{15}$ 8) $\frac{9}{12}$ 9) $\frac{15}{20}$

10) $\frac{4}{10}$ 11) $\frac{6}{14}$ 12) $\frac{8}{12}$

13) $\frac{12}{18}$ 14) $\frac{10}{15}$ 15) $\frac{9}{15}$

16) Cancel down each of these fractions and say which have the value of $\frac{2}{3}$.

$\frac{12}{15}, \frac{8}{10}, \frac{7}{14}, \frac{6}{9}, \frac{6}{12}, \frac{8}{12}, \frac{10}{15}, \frac{14}{30}, \frac{12}{18}, \frac{12}{20}, \frac{4}{6}, \frac{5}{15},$
$\frac{16}{20}, \frac{18}{27}, \frac{14}{21}$

17) Cancel down each of these fractions and list them in order of size, smallest first

$\frac{12}{30}, \frac{12}{15}, \frac{5}{25}, \frac{12}{20}$

Mixed Numbers

Example 1

Each of these parts is $\frac{1}{3}$

The three thirds together make one whole circle.

Write three thirds as $\frac{3}{3}$

$$\frac{3}{3} = 1 \text{ whole}$$

Also $\frac{5}{5} = 1$ $\frac{4}{4} = 1$ $\frac{2}{2} = 1$ and so on.

Example 2

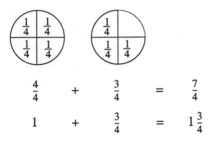

$\frac{4}{4}$	$+$	$\frac{3}{4}$	$= \frac{7}{4}$
1	$+$	$\frac{3}{4}$	$= 1\frac{3}{4}$

The diagram shows that $\frac{7}{4}$ (seven quarters) are equal to $1\frac{3}{4}$

$1\frac{3}{4}$ is an example of a mixed number. It is a mixture of a whole number and a fraction.

$\frac{7}{4}$ is called a top heavy fraction (or an improper fraction).

Example 3

To change $\frac{17}{5}$ into a mixed number.

Divide the top number by the bottom number.

$$17 \div 5 = 3 \text{ remainder } 2$$
$$\text{So } \frac{17}{5} = 3\frac{2}{5}$$

In words: Seventeen fifths make three whole ones with two fifths left over.

Example 4

$$\frac{13}{4} = 13 \div 4 = 3\frac{1}{4}$$

Example 5

$$\frac{17}{6} = 17 \div 6 = 2\frac{5}{6}$$

Exercise 1

Change these top heavy fractions into mixed numbers.

1) $\frac{12}{5}$ 2) $\frac{7}{2}$ 3) $\frac{10}{3}$ 4) $\frac{11}{4}$

5) $\frac{15}{4}$ 6) $\frac{17}{3}$ 7) $\frac{21}{5}$ 8) $\frac{27}{8}$

9) $\frac{31}{9}$ 10) $\frac{47}{10}$ 11) $\frac{41}{7}$ 12) $\frac{33}{13}$

Changing from a mixed number into an improper fraction

Example 6

Change $1\frac{3}{4}$ into an improper fraction

$$1\frac{3}{4} = 1 + \frac{3}{4} = \frac{4}{4} + \frac{3}{4} = \frac{7}{4}$$

Example 7

Change $3\frac{1}{2}$ into an improper fraction

$$3\frac{1}{2} = 3 + \frac{1}{2}$$
$$= \frac{2}{2} + \frac{2}{2} + \frac{2}{2} + \frac{1}{2} = \frac{7}{2}$$

Exercise 2

Change these mixed numbers into improper fractions

1) $1\frac{1}{2}$ 2) $2\frac{1}{4}$ 3) $3\frac{3}{4}$

4) $2\frac{2}{3}$ 5) $2\frac{1}{5}$ 6) $3\frac{1}{7}$

7) $2\frac{3}{4}$ 8) $3\frac{1}{2}$ 9) $2\frac{3}{5}$

10) $2\frac{3}{8}$ 11) $3\frac{5}{7}$ 12) $3\frac{3}{10}$

Adding Fractions

Addition of fractions was touched on earlier in the book. For fractions to be added, their denominators must be the same (see pages 25 and 26)

eg. $\frac{1}{5} + \frac{2}{5} = \frac{3}{5}$

$\frac{9}{15} + \frac{2}{15} = \frac{11}{15}$

and so on.

When the denominators are not the same, we have to make them the same. This is done by changing one or both the fractions into equivalent fractions.

Example 1

$\frac{1}{9} + \frac{1}{3}$

Look at the two denominators. 3 will divide into 9 exactly. So $\frac{1}{3}$ can be written as $\frac{3}{9}$

So $\frac{1}{9} + \frac{1}{3} = \frac{1}{9} + \frac{3}{9} = \frac{4}{9}$

Example 2

$\frac{2}{5} + \frac{1}{4}$

Here 4 will not divide exactly into 5 so we have to look for a number that both 5 and 4 will go into. The smallest number that 5 and 4 will divide into exactly is 20. This is called the LCM (lowest common multiple) of 4 and 5.

So $\frac{2}{5} + \frac{1}{4} = \frac{8}{20} + \frac{5}{20} = \frac{13}{20}$

Example 3

$\frac{1}{4} + \frac{7}{12}$ LCM is 12

$\frac{3}{12} + \frac{7}{12} = \frac{10}{12}$

But $\frac{10}{12}$ is not in its lowest terms. It can be cancelled down by dividing the top and bottom by 2.

i.e. $\frac{10}{12} = \frac{5}{6}$ so $\frac{1}{4} + \frac{7}{12} = \frac{5}{6}$

Exercise
By first finding the LCM of the denominators, calculate each of the following. The first one has been done for you and the next four have their LCM given. Cancel down the answers wherever necessary.

1) $\frac{1}{4} + \frac{1}{6} = \frac{3}{12} + \frac{2}{12} = \frac{5}{12}$

2) $\frac{2}{3} + \frac{1}{6}$ (LCM is 6)

3) $\frac{3}{4} + \frac{1}{12}$ (LCM is 12)

4) $\frac{1}{6} + \frac{1}{8}$ (LCM is 24)

5) $\frac{3}{10} + \frac{2}{15}$ (LCM is 30)

6) $\frac{1}{3} + \frac{1}{5}$ 7) $\frac{2}{7} + \frac{3}{14}$

8) $\frac{3}{5} + \frac{3}{10}$ 9) $\frac{2}{3} + \frac{1}{4}$

10) $\frac{3}{10} + \frac{2}{5}$ 11) $\frac{2}{20} + \frac{3}{10}$

12) $\frac{5}{8} + \frac{1}{6}$ 13) $\frac{3}{10} + \frac{1}{6}$

14) $\frac{7}{12} + \frac{3}{8}$ 15) $\frac{4}{9} + \frac{5}{12}$

16) $\frac{4}{5} + \frac{1}{20}$ 17) $\frac{3}{7} + \frac{5}{21}$

18) $\frac{3}{10} + \frac{5}{25}$ 19) $\frac{5}{8} + \frac{7}{20}$

20) $\frac{3}{8} + \frac{5}{12}$ 21) $\frac{5}{16} + \frac{5}{8}$

Whenever the answer to a question is a top heavy fraction (improper), it should be changed into a mixed number.

Example 1

$$\frac{3}{4} + \frac{1}{2} = \frac{3}{4} + \frac{2}{4} = \frac{5}{4} = 1\frac{1}{4}$$

Example 2

$$\frac{7}{10} + \frac{5}{6} = \frac{21}{30} + \frac{25}{30} = \frac{46}{30} = 1\frac{16}{30} = 1\frac{8}{15}$$

Exercise 1

1) $\frac{3}{4} + \frac{5}{8}$　　　　2) $\frac{7}{10} + \frac{9}{15}$

3) $\frac{8}{9} + \frac{7}{12}$　　　　4) $\frac{7}{9} + \frac{5}{6}$

5) $\frac{3}{4} + \frac{11}{12}$　　　　6) $\frac{5}{8} + \frac{11}{20}$

7) $\frac{7}{8} + \frac{7}{10}$　　　　8) $\frac{4}{5} + \frac{5}{8}$

9) $\frac{7}{11} + \frac{23}{33}$　　　　10) $\frac{7}{12} + \frac{13}{18}$

Adding Mixed Numbers

Always add together the whole number parts separately from the fraction part.

Example 3

$$1\frac{1}{2} + 2\frac{1}{4} = 3 + \left(\frac{1}{2} + \frac{1}{4}\right)$$

$$= 3 + \left(\frac{2}{4} + \frac{1}{4}\right) = 3\frac{3}{4}$$

Example 4

$$2\frac{3}{5} + 4\frac{7}{10} = 6 + \left(\frac{3}{5} + \frac{7}{10}\right)$$

$$= 6 + \left(\frac{6}{10} + \frac{7}{10}\right) = 6\frac{13}{10}$$

But the $\frac{13}{10}$ must be changed to $1\frac{3}{10}$

$$= 6 + 1\frac{3}{10} = 7\frac{3}{10}$$

Exercise 2

1) $1\frac{1}{4} + 2\frac{1}{2}$　　　　2) $3\frac{2}{5} + 1\frac{1}{10}$

3) $2\frac{3}{8} + 1\frac{1}{4}$　　　　4) $5\frac{1}{2} + 3\frac{3}{8}$

5) $2\frac{3}{10} + 1\frac{4}{5}$　　　　6) $5\frac{1}{4} + 6\frac{1}{5}$

7) $5\frac{2}{3} + 6\frac{1}{4}$　　　　8) $4\frac{1}{3} + 3\frac{1}{6}$

9) $5\frac{1}{10} + \frac{3}{5}$　　　　10) $2\frac{5}{8} + 3\frac{3}{4}$

11) $6\frac{3}{4} + 5\frac{5}{8}$　　　　12) $4\frac{1}{16} + 3\frac{3}{4}$

13) $3\frac{2}{5} + 5\frac{9}{10}$　　　　14) $2\frac{7}{8} + 3\frac{1}{4}$

Subtraction

Examples
Using the same method used for addition.

Example 5

$$\frac{3}{4} - \frac{3}{8} = \frac{6}{8} - \frac{3}{8} = \frac{3}{8}$$

Example 6

$$1\frac{3}{4} - \frac{3}{8} = 1 + \left(\frac{3}{4} - \frac{3}{8}\right)$$

$$= 1 + \left(\frac{6}{8} - \frac{3}{8}\right) = 1\frac{3}{8}$$

Example 7

$$3\frac{4}{5} - 2\frac{1}{3} = (3-2) + \left(\frac{4}{5} - \frac{1}{3}\right)$$

$$= 1 + \left(\frac{12}{15} - \frac{5}{15}\right) = 1\frac{7}{15}$$

Exercise 3

1) $\frac{5}{8} - \frac{1}{4}$　　　　2) $\frac{9}{10} - \frac{3}{5}$

3) $\frac{7}{9} - \frac{2}{3}$　　　　4) $1\frac{3}{4} - \frac{2}{3}$

5) $2\frac{7}{8} - \frac{3}{4}$　　　　6) $3\frac{2}{3} - 2\frac{1}{5}$

7) $4\frac{3}{4} - 2\frac{2}{5}$　　　　8) $5\frac{7}{8} - 2\frac{3}{16}$

9) $4\frac{9}{20} - 2\frac{1}{4}$ 10) $5\frac{13}{15} - 3\frac{2}{3}$

11) $4\frac{11}{15} - 1\frac{7}{20}$ 12) $6\frac{5}{6} - 4\frac{1}{4}$

Be careful when the second fraction is bigger than the first fraction.

Example 8

$7\frac{1}{8} - \frac{3}{4} = 7 + \left(\frac{1}{8} - \frac{3}{4}\right) = 7 + \left(\frac{1}{8} - \frac{6}{8}\right)$

Because $\frac{6}{8}$ cannot be taken from $\frac{1}{8}$, we have to 'borrow' a 1 from the 7, then change the 1 into $\frac{8}{8}$.

$6 + \left(1\frac{1}{8} - \frac{3}{4}\right) = 6 + \left(\frac{9}{8} - \frac{6}{8}\right) = 6 + \frac{3}{8} = 6\frac{3}{8}$

Example 9

$$4\frac{1}{4} - 2\frac{3}{5}$$

$$= (4 - 2) + \left(\frac{1}{4} - \frac{3}{5}\right) = 2 + \left(\frac{5}{20} - \frac{12}{20}\right)$$

borrow a 1 from the 2 gives

$$1 + \left(1\frac{5}{20} - \frac{12}{20}\right)$$

$$= 1 + \left(\frac{25}{20} - \frac{12}{20}\right) = 1\frac{13}{20}$$

Exercise 4

In all of these questions you will find the second fraction is bigger than the first.

1) $4\frac{1}{8} - \frac{3}{4}$ 2) $2\frac{1}{2} - \frac{11}{16}$

3) $3\frac{1}{4} - \frac{3}{5}$ 4) $4\frac{1}{8} - 2\frac{3}{4}$

5) $5\frac{1}{10} - 2\frac{3}{5}$ 6) $6\frac{1}{7} - 4\frac{2}{3}$

7) $3\frac{3}{4} - 2\frac{4}{5}$ 8) $4\frac{1}{8} - 1\frac{2}{3}$

9) $6\frac{1}{4} - 3\frac{5}{6}$ 10) $7\frac{1}{7} - 3\frac{1}{3}$

Exercise 5

Mixed Exercise

1) $5\frac{3}{4} - \frac{4}{5}$ 2) $3\frac{14}{15} - 2\frac{2}{3}$

3) $3\frac{1}{2} - 1\frac{5}{6}$ 4) $4\frac{1}{4} - 2\frac{3}{5}$

5) $5\frac{1}{8} - 2\frac{1}{3}$ 6) $4\frac{2}{3} - 2\frac{3}{5}$

7) $1\frac{1}{8} - \frac{7}{16}$ 8) $6\frac{9}{10} - 4\frac{3}{5}$

9) $\frac{8}{9} - \frac{1}{3}$ 10) $5\frac{7}{15} - 2\frac{3}{10}$

11) $4\frac{3}{7} - 1\frac{2}{3}$ 12) $4\frac{9}{10} - 2\frac{7}{20}$

13) $6\frac{2}{7} - 3\frac{2}{3}$ 14) $5\frac{5}{16} - 2\frac{1}{4}$

15) $6\frac{3}{10} - 1\frac{4}{5}$ 16) $8\frac{7}{8} - 2\frac{1}{5}$

Multiplication of Fractions

Multiplying a fraction by a whole number

Example 1

$$\frac{3}{4} \times 2$$

which is 2 lots of $\frac{3}{4}$

or $\frac{3}{4} + \frac{3}{4} = \frac{6}{4} = 1\frac{2}{4} = 1\frac{1}{2}$

Since $\frac{3}{4} \times 2 = \frac{6}{4}$ is the same as $\frac{3}{4} + \frac{3}{4}$, we only multiply the numerator and the denominator remains the same (as shown in 'Adding fractions' on pages 25 and 26)

Example 2

$$\frac{3}{4} \times 6$$

Only the numerator is multiplied by the 6.

$$\frac{3}{4} \times 6 = \frac{18}{4} = 4\frac{2}{4} = 4\frac{1}{2}$$

Example 3

$$1\frac{3}{4} \times 6$$

First change $1\frac{3}{4}$ into the top heavy fraction

$\frac{7}{4}$ then proceed as in example 2

$$\frac{7}{4} \times 6 = \frac{42}{4} = 10\frac{2}{4} = 10\frac{1}{2}$$

Exercise 1

1) $\frac{1}{2} \times 9$ 2) $\frac{3}{8} \times 4$ 3) $\frac{3}{4} \times 7$

4) $\frac{5}{8} \times 4$ 5) $1\frac{3}{8} \times 2$ 6) $2\frac{1}{7} \times 7$

7) $3\frac{1}{2} \times 3$ 8) $5\frac{3}{8} \times 6$ 9) $4\frac{7}{8} \times 5$

10) $6\frac{3}{10} \times 5$ 11) $4\frac{9}{10} \times 6$ 12) $4\frac{1}{8} \times 6$

13) $5\frac{3}{8} \times 7$ 14) $4\frac{3}{5} \times 7$ 15) $2\frac{2}{3} \times 12$

Multiplying a fraction by a fraction

Example 4

$$\frac{3}{4} \times \frac{1}{2}$$

In this case multiply numerator by numerator and denominator by denominator.

$$\frac{3}{4} \times \frac{1}{2} = \frac{3}{8}$$

Example 5

$$\frac{5}{8} \times \frac{3}{4} = \frac{15}{32}$$

Example 6

$$\frac{3}{10} \times \frac{2}{3} = \frac{6}{30} = \frac{1}{5} \text{ (cancel down)}$$

Exercise 2

1) $\frac{3}{4} \times \frac{3}{4}$ 2) $\frac{5}{8} \times \frac{1}{2}$ 3) $\frac{4}{9} \times \frac{2}{3}$

4) $\frac{3}{10} \times \frac{2}{5}$ 5) $\frac{1}{4} \times \frac{5}{8}$ 6) $\frac{3}{5} \times \frac{7}{8}$

7) $\frac{4}{5} \times \frac{2}{3}$ 8) $\frac{6}{7} \times \frac{2}{3}$ 9) $\frac{7}{10} \times \frac{2}{5}$

10) $\frac{3}{4} \times \frac{7}{11}$ 11) $\frac{5}{9} \times \frac{3}{4}$ 12) $\frac{11}{16} \times \frac{2}{3}$

13) $\frac{3}{5} \times \frac{3}{4}$ 14) $\frac{6}{7} \times \frac{1}{3}$ 15) $\frac{5}{9} \times \frac{3}{5}$

16) $\frac{3}{5} \times \frac{2}{7}$ 17) $\frac{5}{7} \times \frac{1}{6}$ 18) $\frac{7}{12} \times \frac{5}{8}$

Multiplying a fraction by a mixed number

To do this, first change the mixed number into an improper fraction.

Example 7

$$\frac{2}{5} \times 1\frac{1}{3} = \frac{2}{5} \times \frac{4}{3} = \frac{8}{15}$$

Example 8

Sometimes the answer is improper so it has to be changed back into a mixed number

$$2\tfrac{1}{2} \times \tfrac{7}{8} = \tfrac{5}{2} \times \tfrac{7}{8} = \tfrac{35}{16} = 2\tfrac{3}{16}$$

Exercise 3

1) $\tfrac{2}{5} \times 1\tfrac{3}{4}$ 　　2) $2\tfrac{1}{3} \times \tfrac{3}{5}$ 　　3) $\tfrac{5}{8} \times 2\tfrac{1}{2}$

4) $\tfrac{3}{8} \times 1\tfrac{3}{10}$ 　　5) $3\tfrac{1}{2} \times \tfrac{5}{6}$ 　　6) $1\tfrac{1}{2} \times \tfrac{3}{10}$

7) $\tfrac{4}{5} \times 1\tfrac{3}{5}$ 　　8) $\tfrac{2}{3} \times 2\tfrac{1}{5}$ 　　9) $3\tfrac{1}{2} \times \tfrac{3}{5}$

10) $4\tfrac{1}{2} \times \tfrac{3}{10}$ 　11) $1\tfrac{3}{5} \times \tfrac{5}{8}$ 　12) $\tfrac{7}{8} \times 3\tfrac{1}{2}$

Sometimes both numbers are mixed so both have to be changed into improper fractions.

Example 9

$$3\tfrac{1}{2} \times 2\tfrac{1}{2} = \tfrac{7}{2} \times \tfrac{5}{2} = \tfrac{35}{4} = 8\tfrac{3}{4}$$

Exercise 4

1) $1\tfrac{1}{2} \times 2\tfrac{1}{2}$ 　2) $1\tfrac{1}{2} \times 2\tfrac{2}{3}$ 　3) $1\tfrac{3}{4} \times 1\tfrac{3}{4}$

4) $2\tfrac{1}{4} \times 3\tfrac{1}{2}$ 　5) $2\tfrac{1}{2} \times 1\tfrac{3}{8}$ 　6) $2\tfrac{1}{8} \times 1\tfrac{1}{5}$

7) $2\tfrac{1}{2} \times 1\tfrac{1}{10}$ 　8) $2\tfrac{1}{4} \times 1\tfrac{1}{2}$ 　9) $3\tfrac{1}{2} \times 1\tfrac{1}{4}$

10) $2\tfrac{3}{10} \times 1\tfrac{1}{4}$ 　11) $4\tfrac{1}{2} \times 3\tfrac{1}{4}$ 　12) $2\tfrac{1}{10} \times 3\tfrac{3}{10}$

Multiplying a mixed number by a whole number

Change the mixed number into an improper fraction and then proceed as before.

Example 10

$$1\tfrac{5}{8} \times 3 = \tfrac{13}{8} \times 3 = \tfrac{39}{8} = 4\tfrac{7}{8}$$

Exercise 5

1) $1\tfrac{1}{2} \times 4$ 　　2) $3\tfrac{1}{2} \times 2$ 　　3) $3 \times 1\tfrac{1}{4}$

4) $5 \times 1\tfrac{1}{10}$ 　　5) $3 \times 1\tfrac{2}{3}$ 　　6) $2\tfrac{1}{2} \times 4$

7) $2\tfrac{1}{4} \times 3$ 　　8) $3\tfrac{1}{2} \times 4$ 　　9) $2\tfrac{1}{5} \times 4$

10) $3 \times 3\tfrac{1}{5}$ 　　11) $5 \times 2\tfrac{3}{4}$ 　12) $6 \times 3\tfrac{2}{5}$

Alternative method for multiplying a mixed number by a whole number

Example 11

$$3\tfrac{7}{10} \times 4$$

Since $3\tfrac{7}{10}$ means $3 + \tfrac{7}{10}$, we can multiply the two parts separately, then add them together.

So $3\tfrac{7}{10} \times 4 = 3 \times 4 + \tfrac{7}{10} \times 4$

$$= 12 + \tfrac{7 \times 4}{10}$$

$$= 12 + \tfrac{28}{10}$$

$$= 12 + 2 + \tfrac{8}{10}$$

$$= 14\tfrac{8}{10} \text{ or } 14\tfrac{4}{5}$$

Example 12

$$4\tfrac{3}{4} \times 1000 = 4000 + \tfrac{3 \times 1000}{4}$$

$$= 4000 + \tfrac{3000}{4}$$

$$= 4000 + 750 = 4750$$

Exercise 6

1) $1\tfrac{1}{2} \times 100$ 　　　2) $3\tfrac{1}{4} \times 20$

3) $2\tfrac{3}{10} \times 15$ 　　　4) $5\tfrac{7}{20} \times 6$

5) $4\tfrac{5}{8} \times 20$ 　　　6) $3\tfrac{4}{5} \times 100$

7) $3\tfrac{7}{8} \times 12$ 　　　8) $2\tfrac{5}{8} \times 20$

9) $4\tfrac{3}{5} \times 16$ 　　　10) $5\tfrac{7}{12} \times 10$

Dividing by a Fraction

This is carried out by inverting the fraction we are dividing by and then multiplying.*

Example

$$3 \div \frac{1}{2}$$

Turn the $\frac{1}{2}$ over to $\frac{2}{1}$ then

$$\frac{3}{1} \times \frac{2}{1} = \frac{6}{1} = 6$$

($\frac{6}{1}$ means 6)

(Think! How many halves in 3 whole ones?)

Example 2

$$2\frac{1}{2} \div 1\frac{1}{4}$$

$$= \frac{5}{2} \div \frac{5}{4}$$

$$= \frac{5}{2} \times \frac{4}{5} = \frac{20}{10} = 2$$

Example 3
Dividing by a whole number

$$3\frac{1}{2} \div 5$$

$$= \frac{7}{2} \div \frac{5}{1} \quad (\frac{5}{1} \text{ means } 5)$$

$$= \frac{7}{2} \times \frac{1}{5} = \frac{7}{10}$$

Exercise

1) $6 \div \frac{1}{2}$

2) $7 \div \frac{1}{3}$

3) $1\frac{1}{2} \div \frac{1}{4}$

4) $2\frac{1}{2} \div \frac{1}{2}$

5) $4\frac{1}{2} \div \frac{1}{4}$

6) $2\frac{1}{2} \div \frac{2}{5}$

7) $3\frac{1}{4} \div 4$

8) $5 \div 1\frac{1}{2}$

9) $2\frac{1}{2} \div 3$

10) $3\frac{1}{4} \div 1\frac{7}{8}$

11) $4 \div 2\frac{1}{2}$

12) $3 \div 2\frac{1}{2}$

13) $5\frac{1}{4} \div 2$

14) $3\frac{1}{2} \div 4$

15) $8\frac{1}{2} \div \frac{1}{3}$

16) $3\frac{2}{5} \div \frac{2}{5}$

17) $4\frac{2}{3} \div 4$

18) $2\frac{1}{4} \div 1\frac{1}{3}$

19) $3\frac{1}{2} \div 2\frac{1}{8}$

20) $\frac{7}{9} \div \frac{3}{4}$

21) $\frac{5}{8} \div 1\frac{1}{4}$

22) $1\frac{5}{8} \div 2\frac{1}{4}$

* Note. There is a proof of this rule which is not necessary to know. My proof is included in the appendix but be warned; some understanding of algebra is needed.

Ratio

A ratio is a way of comparing one quantity with another.

Example 1
Andrew has £12
Betty has £6
We could compare the number of pounds each has by saying
'Andrew has twice as much money as Betty'
or 'Betty has half the amount of money as Andrew'.
Neither of these statements tell us how much each has, they only compare one with another.
Since we know that Andrew has twice as much money as Betty, another way of comparing is to say
'For every two pounds Andrew has, Betty has one'.
This is written down as the ratio
Andrew : Betty = 2:1
Notice the ':' sign and the order 2:1 rather than 1:2
If we change the order of the numbers then we must change the order of the names
i.e. Betty : Andrew = 1:2
Which means that for every pound that Betty has, Andrew has two.

Putting a ratio into its lowest terms
We know from the work on fractions that they must always be quoted in their lowest terms.

i.e. $\frac{2}{4}$ is written as $\frac{1}{2}$

or $\frac{3}{9}$ is written as $\frac{1}{3}$

and so on

The same rule applies to ratio.

Example 2
Christopher has 12 sweets and Debbie has 4 sweets.
So the ratio of the number of Christopher's sweets to Debbie's sweets is
12:4
or ratio C:D = 12:4
or ratio C:D = 3:1
(note the ratio D:C = 1:3)

Example 3
Usha has £1800 in her savings account and Fred has £800 in his account.
Ratio of Usha's savings to Fred's savings is 1800:800
Ratio U:F = 18:8
Ratio U:F = 9:4
Also Ratio F:U = 4:9

Exercise 1
By cancelling down, change these ratios into their lowest terms.

1) 10:5	2) 3:12	3) 15:5
4) 15:6	5) 20:8	6) 9:21
7) 28:21	8) 16:36	9) 12:30
10) 300:50	11) 1000:300	12) 24:100
13) 66:90	14) 45:95	15) 36:84

Splitting up into a given ratio
Example 4
36 sweets are divided between two children, Wesley and Harriet, in the ratio 2:1. How many do they each get?

We know that Wesley is going to get twice as many sweets as Harriet, because his ratio number is 2 and Harriet's is 1.
For every 2 sweets that Wesley gets, Harriet gets 1.
So for every 3 sweets, Wesley gets 2 and Harriet gets 1.
This gives us a method:

35

Suppose we divide the 36 sweets into groups of 3's. Then from each group we give Wesley 2 and Harriet 1.
This can be seen in this diagram

●○○●○●○○●○●○ Wesley's sweets (24)
●○○●○●○○●○●○
●○○●○●○○●○●○ Harriet's sweets (12)

12 groups of 3 sweets

So Wesley gets 24 sweets and Harriet gets 12 sweets.

Numerical method.
Since the ratio is 2:1, we need to divide the sweets into groups of 3 (2+1).

$$36 \div 3 = 12.$$

So there are 12 groups of 3.
From each group, Wesley gets 2 sweets.
So Wesley gets 12×2 sweets = 24 sweets.
From each group Harriet gets 1 sweet.
So Harriet gets 12×1 sweets = 12 sweets.

Example 5
Divide 40 sweets into the ratio 3:2
Step 1   Add together $3 + 2 = 5$
Step 2   Divide $40 \div 5 = 8$
Step 3   First amount is $8 \times 3 = 24$
Step 4   Second amount is $8 \times 2 = 16$
So the 40 sweets are divided into 24 and 16

Exercise 2
Split up the following numbers into the ratio given

1) 30 into the ratio 2:1
2) 45 into the ratio 3:2
3) 20 into the ratio 2:3
4) 30 into the ratio 4:1
5) 50 into the ratio 1:4
6) 60 into the ratio 2:1
7) 60 into the ratio 1:5
8) 80 into the ratio 3:5
9) 80 into the ratio 7:1
10) 70 into the ratio 3:4
11) 70 into the ratio 7:3
12) 100 into the ratio 3:7
13) 250 into the ratio 1:4
14) 350 into the ratio 5:2

Recap Test 2 - Fractions

1) In these diagrams, say what fraction has been shaded in.

a) b) c)

2) In an evening class, there are 12 male students and 13 female students. What fraction of the class are male?

3) Write down these fractions in order of size, smallest first.

$$\frac{1}{2}, \ \frac{1}{7}, \ \frac{1}{4}, \ \frac{1}{6}, \ \frac{1}{12}, \ \frac{1}{3}, \ \frac{1}{5}, \ \frac{1}{9}$$

4) Calculate

a) $\frac{1}{4}$ of 40 b) $\frac{1}{10}$ of 70 c) $\frac{1}{6}$ of 36

d) $\frac{1}{9}$ of 54 e) $\frac{3}{4}$ of 24 f) $\frac{5}{7}$ of 42

g) $\frac{3}{5}$ of 40 h) $\frac{7}{10}$ of 70 i) $\frac{6}{7}$ of 42

5) Calculate

a) $\frac{5}{7} + \frac{1}{7}$ b) $\frac{3}{11} + \frac{4}{11}$ c) $\frac{3}{13} + \frac{7}{13}$

6) Put these fractions into their lowest terms

a) $\frac{3}{9}$ b) $\frac{4}{12}$ c) $\frac{6}{18}$ d) $\frac{9}{12}$

7) Change into mixed numbers

a) $\frac{7}{4}$ b) $\frac{9}{5}$ c) $\frac{13}{6}$ d) $\frac{25}{4}$

8) Change into improper fractions

a) $1\frac{1}{2}$ b) $3\frac{3}{4}$ c) $5\frac{1}{4}$ d) $6\frac{3}{5}$

9) What is the L.C.M. (lowest common multiple) of each of the following pairs of numbers?

a) 4 and 8 b) 8 and 12 c) 6 and 9

10) Calculate

a) $\frac{1}{7} + \frac{1}{21}$ b) $\frac{3}{5} + \frac{3}{10}$ c) $\frac{1}{6} + \frac{1}{12}$

11) Calculate

a) $\frac{1}{2} + \frac{3}{4}$ b) $\frac{7}{8} + \frac{3}{4}$ c) $\frac{4}{5} + \frac{3}{8}$

d) $1\frac{1}{2} + 2\frac{1}{4}$ e) $3\frac{1}{2} + 7\frac{1}{8}$ f) $2\frac{5}{6} + 3\frac{2}{3}$

12) Calculate

a) $\frac{3}{4} - \frac{1}{2}$ b) $\frac{9}{10} - \frac{1}{5}$ c) $\frac{3}{8} - \frac{1}{4}$

d) $2\frac{1}{4} - \frac{1}{2}$ e) $3\frac{3}{8} - \frac{1}{4}$ f) $4\frac{5}{8} - 1\frac{1}{4}$

g) $5\frac{3}{10} - 2\frac{2}{5}$ h) $6\frac{7}{8} - 1\frac{2}{5}$ i) $7\frac{3}{8} - 4\frac{3}{4}$

13) Calculate

a) $\frac{1}{2} \times 7$ b) $\frac{3}{4} \times 10$ c) $4\frac{1}{3} \times 10$

d) $\frac{3}{4} \times 1\frac{1}{2}$ e) $3\frac{1}{2} \times \frac{2}{5}$ f) $1\frac{1}{2} \times 2\frac{1}{2}$

g) $5\frac{1}{7} \times 3\frac{3}{5}$ h) $6\frac{1}{4} \times 2\frac{3}{8}$ i) $5\frac{1}{4} \times 7$

j) $3\frac{1}{2} \times 10$ k) $3\frac{1}{4} \times 100$ l) $6\frac{3}{4} \times 1000$

14) Calculate

a) $6\frac{1}{2} \div \frac{1}{4}$ b) $6\frac{1}{2} \div 4$ c) $\frac{5}{8} \div 2\frac{1}{2}$

15) By cancelling down, change these ratios into their lowest terms.

a) 8:4 b) 9:3 c) 12:8 d) 4:16

16) a) Divide £30 between two people in the ratio 3:2

b) Divide £16.20 between two people in the ratio 7:3.

Decimal Fractions (Decimals)

In the decimal system, only the fractions with denominators of 10, 100, 1000 etc are used. However they are not written in the numerator and denominator form but with a *decimal point*. This point then separates the whole numbers from the fractions.

1) $\frac{9}{10}$ 2) $\frac{9}{100}$ 3) $\frac{19}{100}$ 4) $\frac{39}{100}$

5) $\frac{77}{100}$ 6) $3\frac{3}{10}$ 7) $6\frac{7}{10}$ 8) $24\frac{9}{100}$

9) $28\frac{16}{100}$ 10) $37\frac{53}{100}$ 11) $15\frac{61}{100}$ 12) $76\frac{28}{100}$

Tenths $\frac{1}{10}$

These are written immediately to the right of the decimal point.

$\frac{1}{10}$ is written as 0.1

$\frac{7}{10}$ is written as 0.7

$1\frac{7}{10}$ is written as 1.7

$13\frac{4}{10}$ is written as 13.4

Hundredths $\frac{1}{100}$

These are written immediately to the right of the tenths.

$\frac{1}{100}$ is written as 0.01

$\frac{7}{100}$ is written as 0.07

$1\frac{7}{100}$ is written as 1.07

Hundredths with numerators between 10 and 99 are written as follows

$\frac{11}{100} = \frac{10}{100} + \frac{1}{100} = \frac{1}{10} + \frac{1}{100} = 0.11$ (one tenth and one hundredth)

$\frac{37}{100} = \frac{30}{100} + \frac{7}{100} = \frac{3}{10} + \frac{7}{100} = 0.37$

$5\frac{61}{100} = 5 + \frac{60}{100} + \frac{1}{100} = 5 + \frac{6}{10} + \frac{1}{100} = 5.61$

Exercise 1

Write down each of the following fractions and mixed numbers as decimal numbers.

Thousandths $\frac{1}{1000}$

These are written immediately to the right of the hundredths.

$\frac{1}{1000}$ is written as 0.001

$\frac{7}{1000}$ is written as 0.007

$1\frac{7}{1000}$ is written as 1.007

$\frac{27}{1000} = \frac{20}{1000} + \frac{7}{1000} = \frac{2}{100} + \frac{7}{1000} = 0.027$

$\frac{153}{1000} = \frac{100}{1000} + \frac{50}{1000} + \frac{3}{1000}$

$= \frac{1}{10} + \frac{5}{100} + \frac{3}{1000} = 0.153$

$2\frac{526}{1000} = 2 + \frac{500}{1000} + \frac{20}{1000} + \frac{6}{1000}$

$= 2 + \frac{5}{10} + \frac{2}{100} + \frac{6}{1000} = 2.526$

Ten thousandths $\frac{1}{10000}$

These are written immediately to the right of the thousandths.

– and so on –

Exercise 2

Change these fractions and mixed numbers into decimals.

1) $\frac{7}{1000}$ 2) $\frac{14}{1000}$ 3) $\frac{232}{1000}$ 4) $5\frac{6}{1000}$

5) $18\frac{9}{1000}$ 6) $32\frac{27}{1000}$ 7) $56\frac{348}{1000}$

8) $126\frac{127}{1000}$ 9) $643\frac{80}{1000}$ 10) $54\frac{640}{1000}$

Adding and Subtracting Decimals

Addition

Because decimal fractions are a continuation of the whole number system, addition is carried out in the same way. (see page 10)

Example 1

$$27.3 + 8.614$$

$$
\begin{array}{cc}
27.3 & 27.300 \\
\underline{8.614} & \underline{8.614} \\
 & 35.914
\end{array}
$$
or

Keep the decimal points directly under each other. The positions of the other figures will then line up correctly. The two 'spaces' after the 3 can be filled up with zeros.

Notice that 0.3 or $\frac{3}{10}$

and 0.30 or $\frac{3}{10} + \frac{0}{100} = \frac{3}{10}$

and 0.300 or $\frac{3}{10} + \frac{0}{100} + \frac{0}{1000} = \frac{3}{10}$

are all equal to each other.

Warning Be careful with the zeros. Try to understand which are needed and which are not needed.

Example 2

$183 + 112.8 + 32.614$

Here a decimal point has to be introduced at the end of the 183

$$
\begin{array}{r}
183.000 \\
112.800 \\
\underline{32.614} \\
328.414 \\
\scriptstyle 1 \quad 1
\end{array}
$$

Exercise 1

1) 2.38 + 1.64	2) 15.31 + 8.2
3) 15.81 + 6.315	4) 14.8 + 3.664
5) 127.31 + 8.621	6) 29.14 + 117.6
7) 17.315 + 2.14	8) 18.362 + 6.142
9) 8.326 + 147.6	10) 83 + 6.102

11) 27.36 + 187
12) 125 + 26.41 + 37.314
13) 128.6 + 37.31 + 19
14) 37.145 + 26.1 +73

Subtracting decimals

Again these are carried out in the same way as whole numbers, remembering to keep the decimal points under each other. Either do the decomposition method or the equal addition method. (see page 12)

Example 3

$8.5 - 4.3$

$$
\begin{array}{r}
8.5 \\
\underline{-4.3} \\
4.2
\end{array}
$$

Example 4

$27.4 - 6.1$

$$
\begin{array}{r}
27.4 \\
\underline{-6.1} \\
21.3
\end{array}
$$

Examples 5 and 6 are shown using the *decomposition* method.
Examples 7 and 8 are the same problems using the *equal addition* method.

Example 5

$12.3 - 9.7$ by decomposition

$$
\begin{array}{r}
\overset{0\,^{1}1\,^{1}}{\cancel{1}2.3} \\
\underline{-9.7} \\
2.6
\end{array}
$$

Example 6

37.1 – 6.53 by decomposition

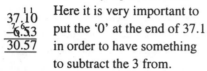

Here it is very important to put the '0' at the end of 37.1 in order to have something to subtract the 3 from.

Example 7

12.3 – 9.7 by equal addition

$$
\begin{array}{r}
1\,2.^{1}3 \\
-\,1_{1}9.7 \\
\hline
2.6
\end{array}
$$

Example 8

37.1 – 6.53 by equal addition

$$
\begin{array}{r}
37.^{1}1^{1}0 \\
-\,6.^{6}53 \\
\hline
30.57
\end{array}
$$

Here it is very important to put the '0' at the end of 37.1 in order to have something to subtract the 3 from.

Exercise 2

1) 7.6 – 4.5

2) 12.7 – 9.3

3) 38.7 – 16.9

4) 24.8 – 2.76

5) 154.3 – 18.6

6) 20 – 8.6

7) 19.41 – 3.7

8) 26.41 – 3.52

9) 56.4 – 17.312

10) 127.6 – 114

11) 37 – 6.415

12) 27.14 – 16.312

13) 38.41 – 17.3

14) 97 – 63.81

Multiplying Decimals

Multiplying decimals by whole numbers

Carry this out using the same method as you did for whole numbers. (see page 17)

Example 1

2.56×3

```
  2.56
 × 3
 7.68
  1 1
```

Notice that there are 2 places after the decimal point in the question (2.56) and 2 places after the decimal point in the answer (7.68)

Don't put the decimal point in until you have completed the answer line.

Exercise 1

1) 2.4×7 2) 5.4×9 3) 6.13×5

4) 4.312×6 5) 3.4×5 6) 5.4×7

7) 4.31×4 8) 18.6×9 9) 37.4×8

10) 3.87×5 11) 15.3×7 12) 23.9×3

Multiplying a decimal by a decimal

Example 2

4.3×0.6

First multiply as if they were both whole numbers.

```
  4.3      There are two places behind the
× 0.6      decimal points in the question.
 2.58      So there have to be two places behind
  ↑↑       the decimal point in the answer.
two places
```

So $4.3 \times 0.6 = 2.58$

Example 3

4.8×5.3

```
 4   Carry over numbers
 2
 4.8    There are two places behind the
× 5.3   decimal points in the question.
 144 }  Don't put any decimal points in here.
2400 }  They will just cause confusion.
25.44
  ↑↑
two places after the decimal point
```

Example 4

4.38×4.5

```
 1 3
 1 4
 4.38 ]  Notice how the numbers are laid out.
× 4.5 }  There is no need to keep the decimal
2190 ]   points under each other.
17520
19.710
 ↑↑↑
three places after the decimal point
```

Example 5

27×0.02

```
  27 ]  Two places behind the
× 0.02 } decimal point.
 0.54   Two places behind the decimal point.
  1
```

Example 6

12.41×5.3

```
 1 2
 1
12.4 1
× 5.3
3723
62050
65.773
```

Exercise 2

1) 4.2×5.3 2) 9.8×2.5

3) 8.6×4.1 4) 9.21×0.7

5) 6.83×0.9 6) 14.1×0.6

7) 24.1×3.2 8) 5.83×7.2

9) 44.3×8.4 10) 7.8×0.05

11) 12.6×0.04 12) 37.3×0.15

13) 84.3×0.28 14) 77.6×5.7

15) 0.45×0.63 16) 0.4×0.316

17) 0.45×0.814 18) 7.3×0.044

More Examples.

Example 7

$$0.3 \times 0.04$$

When dealing with a number like this, first multiply the figures together.

$$\begin{array}{r} 0.3 \\ \times\,0.04 \\ \hline 12 \end{array}$$

The position of the decimal point is found by counting three positions from the right. As there are only two positions in the answer, an extra 0 is introduced to indicate the three positions.

$$\begin{array}{r} 0.3 \\ \times\,0.04 \\ \hline 0.012 \end{array}$$

Example 8

$$0.0034 \times 12$$

$\left.\begin{array}{r} 0.0034 \\ \times\,12 \end{array}\right\}$ Four places after the decimal point

$\begin{array}{r} 68 \\ 340 \\ \hline 0.0408 \\ {\scriptstyle 1} \end{array}$ Four places after the decimal point

Example 9

$$0.015 \times 0.0053$$

$\left.\begin{array}{r} {\scriptstyle 2} \\ {\scriptstyle 1} \\ 0.015 \\ \times\,0.0053 \end{array}\right\}$ Seven places

$\left.\begin{array}{r} 45 \\ 750 \end{array}\right\}$ No decimal point is needed in the calculation part

$\overline{0.0000795}$ Seven places

Example 10

$$27.4 \times 0.0036$$

$\left.\begin{array}{r} {\scriptstyle 2\,1} \\ {\scriptstyle 4\,2} \\ 27.4 \\ \times\,0.0036 \end{array}\right\}$ Five places

$\left.\begin{array}{r} 1644 \\ 8220 \end{array}\right\}$ Calculation part

$\overline{0.09864}$ Five places

Exercise 3

1) 0.03×0.7 2) 0.41×0.3

3) 0.861×0.9 4) 0.14×0.32

5) 0.62×0.48 6) 0.531×0.04

7) 0.61×0.82 8) 0.9×0.681

9) 0.013×0.045 10) 0.021×0.0031

11) 3.4×0.014 12) 8.6×0.003

13) 14×0.006 14) 18.6×0.0014

42

Multiplying and Dividing by 10, 100, 1000 etc

Decimal fractions are an extension of the whole number system which is based on 10. Place values to the right of the decimal point continue to decrease in value by 10 times.

H	T	U	.	$\frac{1}{10}$	$\frac{1}{100}$	$\frac{1}{1000}$	
2	0	0					Two hundreds
	2	0					Twenty or two tens
		2					Two or two units
		0	.	2			Two tenths
		0	.	0	2		Two hundredths
		0	.	0	0	2	Two thousandths

For example

200 is 10 times bigger than 20

20 is 10 times bigger than 2

2 is 10 times bigger than 0.2

0.2 is 10 times bigger than 0.02

0.02 is 10 times bigger than 0.002

- and so on -

To divide a number by 10, move the number to the right by one place

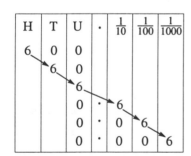

$600 \div 10 = 60$

$60 \div 10 = 6$

$6 \div 10 = 0.6$

$0.6 \div 10 = 0.06$

$0.06 \div 10 = 0.006$

Likewise

$7 \div 10 = 0.7$

$0.81 \div 10 = 0.081$

$27.3 \div 10 = 2.73$

$0.8 \div 10 = 0.08$

$4.31 \div 10 = 0.431$

$0.105 \div 10 = 0.0105$

Rule

When dividing by 10 move each of the figures one place to the right relative to the decimal point.

Exercise 1

Divide each of the following numbers by 10.

1) 300
2) 40
3) 8
4) 310
5) 77
6) 6.5
7) 317
8) 67.4
9) 7.54
10) 0.6
11) 0.13
12) 0.407
13) 1.6
14) 1.73
15) 71.5
16) 106.4
17) 38.21
18) 27.4
19) 0.003
20) 0.8135
21) 0.0104

To divide a number by 100, move the number to the right two places relative to the decimal point

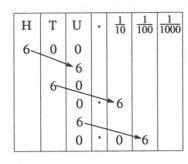

$600 \div 100 = 6$

$60 \div 100 = 0.6$

$6 \div 100 = 0.06$

Likewise

$126 \div 100 = 1.26$

$37 \div 100 = 0.37$

$7 \div 100 = 0.07$

$27.3 \div 100 = 0.273$

$3.4 \div 100 = 0.034$

$0.135 \div 100 = 0.00135$

From what has been done so far, a *general rule* can now be used. This rule is the one I find people remember best. Instead of moving the *figures* to the right, move the *decimal point* to the left.

___

When dividing by powers of 10, move the decimal point to the left the same number of places there are zeros

___

Rule
When dividing by 100 move each of the figures two places to the right relative to the decimal point.

Example1
$27.4 \div 10 = 2.74$
↑   ← move the point 1 place
1 zero

Exercise 2
Divide each of the following numbers by 100.

1) 3,000	2) 500	3) 70
4) 8	5) 3100	6) 470
7) 57	8) 8.2	9) 4120
10) 653	11) 60.5	12) 7.31
13) 3142	14) 0.6	15) 0.014
16) 0.156	17) 3.14	18) 16.03
19) 0.095	20) 1.003	21) 0.002

Example 2
$57.3 \div 100 = 0.573$
↑↑   ← move the point 2 places
2 zeros

Example 3
$6 \div 1000 = 6.0 \div 1000 = 0.006$
↑↑↑   ←move 3 places
3 zeros

Example 4
$0.153 \div 100 = 0.00153$

Example 5
$6.41 \div 1000 = 0.00641$

Example 6
$73 \div 10 = 7.3$

Exercise 3
Write down the answers to each of these.

1) $2.68 \div 100$	2) $6.41 \div 10$
3) $9.62 \div 100$	4) $12.52 \div 100$
5) $6.7 \div 10$	6) $9.4 \div 100$
7) $8.63 \div 1000$	8) $20.4 \div 100$
9) $0.31 \div 10$	10) $0.9 \div 100$
11) $0.8 \div 1000$	12) $0.61 \div 10$
13) $0.83 \div 100$	14) $0.43 \div 1000$
15) $0.06 \div 10$	16) $0.08 \div 100$
17) $6.09 \div 1000$	18) $26.4 \div 1000$
19) $176 \div 1000$	20) $19.4 \div 1000$

Multiplying by powers of 10

Consider this
$$200 \div 10 = 20$$
$$\text{and } 20 \times 10 = 200$$

Similarly $210 \div 10 = 21$
$$\text{and } 21 \times 10 = 210$$

Also $215 \div 10 = 21.5$
$$\text{and } 21.5 \times 10 = 215$$
So multiplication is the reverse of division.

Rule
When multiplying by powers of 10, move the decimal point to the right the same number of places there are zeros

Example 7
$8.3 \times 10 = 83. = 83$
↑   move one place
1 zero

Example 8
$0.845 \times 100 = 84.5$
↑↑   move two places
2 zeros

Example 9
$0.814 \times 1000 = 814.0 = 814$
↑↑↑   move three places
3 zeros

Example 10
$0.015 \times 10 = 0.15$

Example 11
$0.0003 \times 100 = 0.03$

Example 12
$12.143 \times 100 = 1214.3$

Exercise 4

1) 0.3×10	2) 0.14×10
3) 1.31×10	4) 0.16×100
5) 0.4×100	6) 0.08×100
7) 1.3×100	8) 2.9×1000
9) 8.16×1000	10) 27.41×10
11) 106.7×100	12) 0.00081×1000
13) 6.003×10	14) 10.01×100
15) 18.76×1000	16) 4.31×10
17) 6.014×100	18) 0.87×1000
19) 8.71×1000	20) 8.014×1000

Dividing Decimals

There are two types of answers that can be obtained when dividing;
a) those with a remainder and
b) those with decimals.
Both types make sense.

Consider these two examples

1) If 28 tropical fish are divided equally amongst 5 people, they would each get 5 fish and there would be 3 fish left over.

2) If a length of rope measuring 28 metres is cut into 5 equal parts, each part would measure 5.6 metres.

Both questions are division. Both use the same numbers, but their answers need to be interpreted differently.

In this section we will concentrate on problems of type 2.

When dividing to get decimal answers, we proceed in the same general way as for whole numbers (see page 18). However, after the decimal point (to the right) we can put in as many zeros as we like. This allows us to keep on dividing until we get the answer we want

Example 1

$$28 \div 5$$

step 1

$$5\overline{)2\,8}$$ 5

At this point there is a remainder of 3.

step 2

$$5\overline{)2\,8\,\overset{3}{.}0}$$ 5

Now put in the decimal point with a zero behind it and carry over the 3.

This can be done because 28, 28., 28.0, 28.00 etc all have the same value

They mean 28 whole units and no fractions.

step 3

$$5\overline{)2\,8\,\overset{3}{.}0}$$ $5\cdot6$

The decimal point in the answer is put above the decimal point in the question.

Example 2

$$38 \div 8$$

step 1

$$8\overline{)3\,8}$$ $4\;r6$

step 2

$$8\overline{)3\,8\,\overset{6}{.}0}$$ $4.$

Introduce the decimal point and zero after it. Carry over the 6.

step 3

$$8\overline{)3\,8\,\overset{6}{.}0\overset{4}{0}}$$ 4.7

Divide, then introduce another zero and carry over the 4.

step 4

$$8\overline{)3\,8\,\overset{6}{.}0\overset{4}{0}}$$ $4.7\,5$

So $38 \div 8 = 4.75$ or 4 remainder 6

Example 3
This process can also be done with decimal numbers

$$28.1 \div 5$$

$$5\overline{)2\,8\,\overset{3}{.}1\overset{1}{0}}$$ $5\cdot6\,2$

So $28.1 \div 5 = 5.62$

Example 4

$$0.62 \div 8$$

$$8\overline{)0.6\,2\,\overset{6}{0}\overset{4}{0}}$$ $.0\,7\,7\,5$

So $0.62 \div 8 = 0.0775$

Notice that we start this by saying 8 into 6 goes zero times (with 6 left over). Then say 8 divided into 62.

Example 5

$2.001 \div 5$

$$5\overline{)2.0010}\quad\begin{array}{l}0.4002\end{array}$$

Remember to put down zero when 5 won't go into the number.

So $2.001 \div 5 = 0.4002$

Exercise 1

1) $27 \div 5$	2) $31 \div 4$
3) $42 \div 8$	4) $43.2 \div 8$
5) $41 \div 5$	6) $44.1 \div 7$
7) $50.4 \div 6$	8) $27 \div 4$
9) $0.192 \div 8$	10) $14.4 \div 9$
11) $1.05 \div 5$	12) $132.6 \div 6$
13) $19.5 \div 6$	14) $41.84 \div 8$
15) $31.85 \div 7$	16) $0.1 \div 8$
17) $4.002 \div 5$	18) $12.09 \div 6$
19) $56.12 \div 4$	20) $112.5 \div 9$

Changing a fraction into a decimal

Consider this:

Three pies are divided equally amongst four people.

Divide each pie into four equal parts

Now we have 12 quarters to share amongst 4 people. So they will each get 3 quarters.

So $3 \div 4$ is $\frac{3}{4}$

i.e. When 3 pies are divided equally amongst 4 people they each get $\frac{3}{4}$ of a pie.

So this can be done without drawing pictures

i.e. $3 \div 4 = \frac{3}{4}$

Similarly $7 \div 8 = \frac{7}{8}$

and $9 \div 10 = \frac{9}{10}$

and so on

So a fraction is another way of showing a division.

Example 5

Change $\frac{7}{8}$ into a decimal fraction.

Since we know that $\frac{7}{8}$ is the same as $7 \div 8$

then $\frac{7}{8} = \dfrac{0.875}{8\overline{)7.0^60^40}}$

$\frac{7}{8} = 0.875$

The rule for changing a fraction into a decimal is to divide the numerator by the denominator.

Example 6

$$\frac{9}{10} = \dfrac{0.9}{10\overline{)9.0}} = 0.9$$

Example 7

$$\frac{3}{4} = \dfrac{0.75}{4\overline{)3.0^20}} = 0.75$$

Example 8

$$\frac{1}{8} = \dfrac{0.125}{8\overline{)1.0^20^40}} = 0.125$$

Exercise 2

Change each of the following fractions into decimals

1) $\frac{1}{5}$	2) $\frac{1}{2}$	3) $\frac{3}{10}$
4) $\frac{7}{10}$	5) $\frac{3}{8}$	6) $\frac{3}{5}$
7) $\frac{5}{8}$	8) $\frac{1}{4}$	9) $\frac{7}{8}$
10) $\frac{1}{25}$	11) $\frac{3}{20}$	12) $\frac{3}{40}$
13) $\frac{7}{20}$	14) $\frac{1}{40}$	15) $\frac{5}{16}$

Rounding off Decimals

(see page 20 for rounding off whole numbers and later pages 54 to 56 for a fuller version of rounding off)

Sometimes fractions don't change into decimals easily.

For example

$\frac{1}{3}$ is $1 \div 3 = $ $\begin{array}{r} 0.3\,3\,3\,3 \\ 3\overline{)1 \cdot 0^{1}0^{1}0^{1}0^{1}} \end{array}$

In this case we keep having to carry 1 so the 3 will continue for ever. When we see this happening we have to take this into account when writing down the answer. We could just use the first two decimal places and say

$\frac{1}{3} = 0.33$

or use the first three decimal places

$\frac{1}{3} = 0.333$

and so on.

This depends on how accurate we want the answer to be. 0.333 is more accurate than 0.33. But if the answer referred to money, then £0.33 would represent 33 pence and would therefore make more sense than £0.333.

Rounding off to two decimal places

The following examples show what would happen if the decimal part is rounded off to 2 decimal places.

1.613 becomes 1.61

15.5813 becomes 15.58

0.314 becomes 0.31

9.541582 becomes 9.54

and so on

However. If the third decimal place has a 5 or more in it, then the second decimal place is increased by 1.

Examples

0.54**8** becomes 0.55

0.64**9**13 becomes 0.65

27.61**5**01 becomes 27.62

6.08**7**1 becomes 6.09

Think of pounds and pence and round off to the nearest penny.

There is one situation that sometimes causes confusion

8.29**6**2 becomes 8.30

This is why.

Since 1 is to be added to the second decimal place, we get this

$\begin{array}{r} 8.29 \\ + 0.01 \\ \hline 8.30 \\ {\scriptstyle 1} \end{array}$

so be careful.

Exercise 1
Round off each of the following to 2 decimal places.

1) 1.331	2) 8.9384	3) 0.6182
4) 9.3825	5) 19.5112	6) 2.813
7) 0.031	8) 0.497	9) 6.9381
10) 0.7893	11) 4.183	12) 14.4891
13) 14.562	14) 2.8181	15) 0.0761
16) 8.6793	17) 6.3676	18) 3.197

Lets look back at changing $\frac{1}{3}$ into a decimal.

If this has to be written correct to 2 decimal places, we have to keep dividing until we have three decimal places. The third decimal place will tell us whether to change the second decimal place or not.

So $\frac{1}{3} = 3\overline{)1 \cdot 0^1 0^1 0}$ with quotient $0 \cdot 3\ 3\ 3$

or $\frac{1}{3} = 0.33$ to 2 decimal places

Other examples

1) $\frac{2}{3} = 3\overline{)2 \cdot 0^2 0^2 0}$ with quotient $0 \cdot 6\ 6\ 6$

So $\frac{2}{3} = 0.67$ to 2 decimal places

2) $\frac{2}{7} = 7\overline{)2 \cdot 0^6 0^4 0}$ with quotient $0 \cdot 2\ 8\ 5$

So $\frac{2}{7} = 0.29$ to 2 decimal places

3) $\frac{5}{9} = 9\overline{)5 \cdot 0^5 0^5 0}$ with quotient $0 \cdot 5\ 5\ 5$

So $\frac{5}{9} = 0.56$ to 2 decimal places.

4) $\frac{5}{11} = 11\overline{)5 \cdot 0^6 0^5 0}$ with quotient $0 \cdot 4\ 5\ 4$

So $\frac{5}{11} = 0.45$ to 2 decimal places.

Exercise 2

Change each of the following into decimals correct to 2 decimal places.

1) $\frac{7}{9}$ 2) $\frac{7}{11}$ 3) $\frac{3}{11}$

4) $\frac{3}{7}$ 5) $\frac{4}{11}$ 6) $\frac{2}{11}$

7) $\frac{1}{7}$ 8) $\frac{1}{9}$ 9) $\frac{6}{7}$

10) $\frac{4}{7}$ 11) $\frac{2}{9}$ 12) $\frac{1}{11}$

13) $\frac{4}{9}$ 14) $\frac{5}{7}$ 15) $\frac{8}{9}$

Percentages

The third way of writing down a part of something is as a percentage (the others are fractions and decimals).

Percentages are hundredths.

$\frac{1}{100}$ is 1 percent (1%)

$\frac{50}{100}$ or $\frac{1}{2}$ is 50 percent (50%)

and so on.

The following percentages, expressed as fractions are worth remembering as lots of calculations need them.

$1\% = \frac{1}{100}$

$10\% = \frac{10}{100} = \frac{1}{10}$

$20\% = \frac{20}{100} = \frac{1}{5}$

$25\% = \frac{25}{100} = \frac{1}{4}$

$50\% = \frac{50}{100} = \frac{1}{2}$

$75\% = \frac{75}{100} = \frac{3}{4}$

$33\frac{1}{3}\% = \frac{33\frac{1}{3}}{100} = \frac{100}{300} = \frac{1}{3}$

$66\frac{2}{3}\% = \frac{66\frac{2}{3}}{100} = \frac{200}{300} = \frac{2}{3}$

These can be used to calculate simple percentage problems

Example 1

$$50\% \text{ of } £6$$

$\frac{1}{2}$ of £6 is £6 ÷ 2 = £3

Example 2

$$10\% \text{ of } £3.40$$

$\frac{1}{10}$ of £3.40 = £3.40 ÷ 10 = £0.34 = 34p

(remember when dividing by 10 to move the decimal point)

Example 3

$$75\% \text{ of } £6$$

i.e. $\frac{3}{4}$ of £6

$\frac{1}{4}$ of £6 = £6 ÷ 4 = £1.50

$\frac{3}{4}$ of £6 = £1.50 × 3 = £4.50

Example 4

$$15\% \text{ of } £8.60$$

10% of £8.60 = £0.86 = 86p

5% of £8.60 = £0.43 = 43p (half of 10%)

So 15% of £8.60 = 86p + 43p

$$= 129p \text{ or } £1.29$$

Example 5

$$17\frac{1}{2}\% \text{ of } £10.40$$

10% of £10.40 = £1.04   move the point.

5% of £10.40 = £0.52   half of 10%

$2\frac{1}{2}\%$ of £10.40 = £0.26   half of 5%

So $17\frac{1}{2}\%$ of £10.40

$$= £1.04 + 52p + 26p = £1.82$$

Exercise 1

Calculate each of the following in the way shown above

1) 50% of £6.80

2) 10% of £9.50

3) 25% of £8.00

4) 75% of £10.00

5) 75% of £16.20

6) 15% of £4.00

7) 15% of £6.40

8) 5% of £4.20

9) $2\frac{1}{2}\%$ of £4.00

10) $7\frac{1}{2}\%$ of £10.00

11) $17\frac{1}{2}\%$ of £20

12) $17\frac{1}{2}\%$ of £24

To calculate a percentage of something

This method will always work. Use it where the percentages are not simple.

Example 6

Calculate 6% of 750

$$1\% \text{ of } 750$$
$$= \frac{1}{100} \text{ of } 750$$

Now carry on as if you were finding a fraction of something.

$$= 750 \div 100 = 7.5$$
$$\text{so } 6\% = 7.5 \times 6 = 45.0 \text{ or } 45$$
$$\text{i.e. } 6\% \text{ of } 750 \text{ is } 45$$

Example 7

Calculate 57% of 900

$$1\% \text{ of } 900$$
$$= 900 \div 100 = 9$$
$$\text{so } 57\% \text{ of } 900 = 57 \times 9 = 513$$
$$\text{i.e. } 57\% \text{ of } 900 = 513$$

Example 8

Calculate 16% of £5.50

$$\text{Let £5.50 be 550 pence}$$
$$1\% \text{ of } 550 = 5.5$$
$$\text{so } 16\% = 16 \times 5.5 = 88$$
$$\text{i.e. } 16\% \text{ of £5.50 is 88 pence}$$

Example 9

Calculate 55% of £4.20

$$1\% \text{ of £4.20}$$
$$= 420 \div 100 = 4.2 \text{ pence}$$
$$\text{so } 55\% = 55 \times 4.2 = 231 \text{ pence}$$
$$\text{i.e. } 55\% \text{ of £4.20 is £2.31}$$

To calculate a percentage of something, divide by 100 then multiply by the percentage

---

Example 10

Calculate 44% of £6.00

$$600 \text{ pence } \div 100 \times 44$$
$$= 6 \times 44 = 264 \text{ pence}$$
$$= £2.64$$

Example 11

Calculate 18% of £12.50

$$1250 \text{ pence } \div 100 \times 18$$
$$= 12.5 \times 18 = 225 \text{ pence}$$
$$= £2.25$$

Exercise 2

Calculate each of the following by first calculating 1%.

1) 8% of 700	2) 11% of 500
3) 17% of 400	4) 32% of 650
5) 47% of 900	6) 56% of 250
7) 65% of 620	8) 72% of 225
9) 83% of £16	10) 92% of £8
11) 43% of £12	12) 16% of £3.50
13) 87% of £14	14) 36% of £9.50
15) 45% of £4.40	16) 58% of £6.50

Changing Information into a Percentage

Example 1

Eddie travels 200 kilometres from his home to London. 160 kilometres is driven on a motorway. What percentage of his journey is on the motorway?

Using the figures given, we can say that the fraction of Eddie's journey on the motorway is 160 km out of a total of 200 km or

$$\frac{160}{200}$$

This will cancel down to $\frac{16}{20}$ by dividing both the numerator and denominator by 10. It will further cancel down to $\frac{4}{5}$ by dividing both numerator and denominator by 4. Now change this into a decimal by dividing the numerator by the denominator.

$$\frac{4}{5} = 4 \div 5 = 0.8$$

Then into a percentage by multiplying by 100

$$0.8 = 0.8 \times 100 = 80\%$$

So Eddie has travelled 80% of his journey on the motorway.

Example 2

Kirsty gets a mark of 12 out of 20 in her maths test. What is this as a percentage?

As a fraction she gets $\frac{12}{20}$

This can be simplified to $\frac{3}{5}$ by dividing the numerator and denominator by 4.

$$\frac{3}{5} = 3 \div 5 = 0.6$$
$$0.6 = 0.6 \times 100\% = 60\%$$

So Kirsty gets a mark of 60%

Example 3

A country has a population of 20 million. 11,500,000 are female and 8,500,000 are male. What percentage are female?

As a fraction $\frac{11,500,000}{20,000,000}$

Simplifying gives $\frac{115}{200}$ (i.e. by dividing top and bottom by 100,000)

$$\frac{115}{200} = \frac{23}{40}$$
$$\frac{23}{40} = 23 \div 40 = 0.575$$
$$0.575 = 0.575 \times 100\% = 57.5\%$$

So the percentage of the population that are females is 57.5%.

Exercise

Change each of the following into a percentage.

1) A car travels to London, a distance of 250 kilometres. The driver stops for a rest after 50 kilometres. What percentage of the journey has been completed?

2) A train breaks down after completing 60 kilometres of a 150 kilometre journey. What percentage of the journey has it travelled?

3) Mrs O'Neill earns £160. She pays £48 tax. What percentage of her earnings is paid in tax?

4) Change each of the following test marks into percentages.

a) 57 out of 100   b) 18 out of 20
c) 7 out of 10   d) 30 out of 50
e) 35 out of 50   f) 12 out of 40
g) 24 out of 40   h) 120 out of 200

5) In a town there are 10,000 inhabitants. If there are 4,500 males, what percentage of the population are male?

Fractions, Decimals and Percentages

(see also changing fractions into decimals on page 47)

This diagram represents the steps involved in changing from one type of fraction to another.

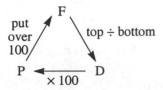

To change a fraction into a decimal, divide the numerator by the denominator.
To change a decimal into a percentage, multiply by 100.
To change a percentage into a fraction, write it as a fraction over 100, then cancel down.

Example 1

Change $\frac{3}{5}$ into a decimal $\quad$ F $\longrightarrow$ D

$$3 \div 5 = 0.6$$

Example 2

Change $\frac{4}{5}$ into a percentage

$$F \longrightarrow D \longrightarrow P$$
$$4 \div 5 = 0.8$$
$$0.8 \times 100 = 80\%$$

Example 3

Change 0.825 into a percentage

$$D \longrightarrow P$$
$$0.825 \times 100 = 82.5\%$$

Example 4

Change 73% into a fraction

$$P \longrightarrow F$$
$$73\% = \frac{73}{100}$$

Example 5

Change 85% into a fraction

$$P \longrightarrow F$$
$$85\% = \frac{85}{100}$$

Divide numerator and denominator by 5

$$\frac{85}{100} = \frac{17}{20}$$

So 85% is $\frac{17}{20}$

Example 6

Change 0.71 into a fraction

$$D \longrightarrow P \longrightarrow F$$
$$0.71 \times 100 = 71\%$$
$$71\% = \frac{71}{100}$$

Exercise

Change each of the following

1) $\frac{2}{5}$ into a decimal
2) 0.31 into a percentage
3) 70% into a fraction
4) 90% into a fraction
5) 95% into a fraction
6) $\frac{7}{8}$ into a percentage
7) 25% into a fraction
8) 0.85 into a percentage
9) 0.725 into a percentage
10) $\frac{3}{10}$ into a percentage
11) $\frac{3}{4}$ into a decimal
12) 62% into a fraction
13) 0.45 into a percentage
14) 45% into a fraction
15) 0.83 into a fraction
16) $\frac{4}{5}$ into a percentage
17) 0.35 into a fraction
18) $\frac{7}{10}$ into a percentage
19) 0.82 into a fraction
20) 0.875 into a percentage

Rounding off Decimal Numbers

First look at the section 'Rounding off Decimals' on page 48.

Rounding off to the nearest whole number

Consider the numbers 87 and 83.
If 87 is rounded off to the nearest 10 it becomes 90.
If 83 is rounded off to the nearest 10 it becomes 80.
Similarly if 8.7 is rounded off to the nearest whole number it becomes 9 (not 9.0 for reasons I will explain later) and 8.3 is rounded off to 8

All the tenths between 8 and 9 look like this

8.1 8.2 8.3 8.4 | 8.5 8.6 8.7 8.8 8.9

| All these are rounded <u>down</u> to 8 | All these are rounded <u>up</u> to 9 |

Anything that is 8.5 or bigger will round up to 9.
Anything that is less than 8.5 rounds down to 8.

Exercise 1
Round off each of the following to the nearest whole number.

1) 6.4	2) 7.8	3) 9.3
4) 10.7	5) 3.4	6) 19.2
7) 21.7	8) 16.2	9) 12.5
10) 37.9	11) 4.3	12) 19.7

Examples
8.45 becomes 8
        (only consider the 4, ignore the 5)
19.46 becomes 19
27.83 becomes 28
and so on.

Exercise 2
Round off each of the following to the nearest whole number.

1) 8.33	2) 9.42	3) 12.74
4) 8.68	5) 13.55	6) 23.48
7) 37.81	8) 51.94	9) 59.94
10) 87.63	11) 4.98	12) 6.43
13) 8.55	14) 12.42	15) 19.99

When rounding off to any decimal number correct to the nearest whole number, only consider the first decimal place.

8 . **4**	becomes 8
8 . **7**	becomes 9
6 . **4** 3	becomes 6
6 . **8** 3	becomes 7
1 8 . **4** 3 1	becomes 18
1 8 . **9** 7 9	becomes 19
2 7 . **1** 5 3 1	becomes 27
3 5 . **7** 1 5 4	becomes 36

↑
Only consider this place.

Exercise 3
Round off each of the following to the nearest whole number.

1) 4.82	2) 9.614	3) 27.61
4) 6.487	5) 137.3	6) 16.4
7) 12.83	8) 9.63	9) 82.91
10) 132.4	11) 12.4812	12) 36.1521
13) 19.4	14) 17.42	15) 47.67

Rounding off to 1 Decimal Place

Consider the numbers 847 and 843.
These become 850 and 840 when rounded off to the nearest 10.
Similarly 8.47 and 8.43 become 8.5 and 8.4 when rounded off to 1 decimal place.
So in order to round off to 1 decimal place we need to consider the figure in the second decimal place.

6 . 4 **3**	becomes 6.4
7 . 8 **8**	becomes 7.9
2 . 4 **8** 3	becomes 2.5
1 6 . 1 **8** 3	becomes 16.2
4 . 8 **3** 6	becomes 4.8
1 2 7 . 4 **1**	becomes 127.4

↑
Consider this figure

Exercise 1
By considering the second decimal place, round off each of these numbers to 1 decimal place.

1) 7.84	2) 6.4814	3) 6.32
4) 19.51	5) 29.4815	6) 3.82
7) 14.85	8) 16.3154	9) 5.46
10) 3.658	11) 27.6821	12) 5.71

Important case
Sometimes more than one figure needs to be changed to get the answer.
Round off 8.961 to 1 decimal place.
In this case the .9 needs to be increased by 0.1. But this makes 1.0, which means that the 8 is increased to 9

$$\begin{array}{r} 8.9 \\ +\ .1 \\ \hline 9.0 \end{array}$$

i.e.

So 8.961, rounded off to 1 decimal place is 9.0.
Note. 9.0 indicates that the number has been rounded off to 1 decimal place.

9 indicates that the number has been rounded off to the nearest whole number. (see the example at the beginning of page 54).
Although 9.0 and 9 have the same value, what they tell us about their accuracy is different, i.e. 9.0 is more accurate than 9.

Examples
When rounding off to 1 decimal place
7.963 becomes 8.0
18.981 becomes 19.0
27.951 becomes 28.0
43.998 becomes 44.0

Exercise 2
Round off each of these numbers to 1 decimal place

1) 6.957	2) 12.984	3) 3.98
4) 5.954	5) 6.9715	6) 8.98761
7) 4.9752	8) 19.9981	9) 10.98
10) 9.9614	11) 8.95	12) 4.9999

Rounding off to any Number of Places

We can now write down a general rule for rounding off numbers

If the figure to the right of the decimal place is 5 or more, increase the figure in the decimal place by 1.
If the figure to the right of the decimal place is less than 5, leave the figure in the decimal place as it is.

Examples
These numbers have been rounded off to the decimal places (d.p.) indicated. The figure which has been considered is the one in bold.

9 . 3 1 **4** 5	9.31 to 2 d.p.
1 2 . 8 **5** 4	12.9 to 1 d.p.
6 . 4 **8** 5 3	6.5 to 1 d.p.
2 0 . 1 4 **8** 3	20.15 to 2 d.p.
9 . 4 **1** 5	9.4 to 1 d.p.
2 2 . 6 7 1 **4**	22.671 to 3 d.p.
8 . 6 9 **8** 2	8.70 to 2 d.p.
0 . 8 3 1 **4**	0.831 to 3 d.p.
0 . 0 6 **5** 3	0.07 to 2 d.p.
0 . 4 8 2 **3**	0.482 to 3 d.p.
0 . 0 0 8 4 **5**	0.0085 to 4 d.p.
0 . 0 9 7 **1** 4	0.10 to 2 d.p.
0 . 9 9 **8** 1 4	1.00 to 2 d.p.

Exercise
Round off each of the following to the number of decimal places indicated.

1) 7.3154   1 d.p.
2) 0.0741   2 d.p.
3) 8.3152   2 d.p.
4) 7.00145   4 d.p.
5) 0.00739   4 d.p.
6) 10.6415   1 d.p.
7) 12.843   2 d.p.
8) 17.417   2 d.p.
9) 9.3145   3 d.p.
10) 16.8543 1 d.p.
11) 9.99831 2 d.p.
12) 6.81403 3 d.p.
13) 0.00903 4 d.p.
14) 0.00881 3 d.p.
15) 3.4854   2 d.p.
16) 2.9697   1 d.p.

1) Write down each of the following as decimal numbers.

a) $\frac{7}{10}$ b) $\frac{17}{100}$ c) $\frac{53}{1000}$

d) $3\frac{3}{10}$ e) $17\frac{3}{100}$ f) $18\frac{9}{1000}$

2) Showing all your work, calculate the following

a) $2.95 + 3.76$ b) $4.82 + 16$
c) $97.31 + 6.821$ d) $193 + 27.5 + 3.6$
e) $19.7 + 40 + 6.013$ f) $17.3 - 2.15$
g) $9.87 - 6.314$ h) $37 - 9.36$

3) Showing all your work, calculate the following.

a) 3.6×9 b) 27.6×4
c) 95.6×0.31 d) 0.7×0.382
e) 0.82×0.9 f) 8.7×0.006

4) Write down the answers to each of the following without doing any calculations.

a) 3.6×10 b) 5.6×100 c) 0.023×10
d) 0.018×1000 e) 2.654×1000
f) 0.153×100 g) 0.2×100

5) Write down the answers to each of the following without doing any calculations.

a) $6 \div 10$ b) $27 \div 10$ c) $43.2 \div 10$
d) $0.8 \div 10$ e) $0.001 \div 10$
f) $52.6 \div 100$ g) $1.84 \div 100$
h) $0.02 \div 100$ i) $2703 \div 1000$

6) Show all your workings. Give your answer as a decimal number.

a) $27 \div 6$ b) $18.5 \div 5$ c) $49.2 \div 4$
d) $0.0091 \div 7$ e) $11.277 \div 9$

7) Change these fractions into decimals Show all your workings.

a) $\frac{3}{4}$ b) $\frac{3}{8}$ c) $\frac{7}{40}$

8) Round off the following, correct to 2 decimal places

a) 3.143   b) 8.694   c) 5.978
d) 12.208   e) 6.995   f) 0.315

9) Calculate

a) 50% of £30   b) 25% of £40
c) 20% of £6   d) 10% of £9

e) 5% of £10   f) $2\frac{1}{2}$% of £100

g) $7\frac{1}{2}$% of £8   h) $17\frac{1}{2}$% of £50

i) 8% of £16   j) 35% of £19

10) In a college there are 2250 men and 2750 women students. What percentage of the students are men?

11) In an examination a student gets a mark of 84 out of 150. What is this as a percentage ?

12) Change;

a) $\frac{3}{5}$ into a decimal

b) 32% into a fraction

c) $\frac{3}{8}$ into a percentage

d) 0.68 into a fraction

e) 0.75 into a percentage

13) Round off to the nearest whole number

a) 27.315   b) 7.931   c) 18.514

14) Round off each of the following correct to the number of decimal places indicated.

a) 8.941 to 1 decimal place
b) 17.8391 to 2 decimal places
c) 0.01842 to 3 decimal places
d) 10.03845 to 4 decimal places

Thermometer Scale (Negative Numbers)

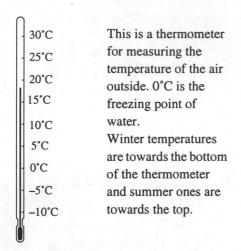

30°C
25°C
20°C
15°C
10°C
5°C
0°C
–5°C
–10°C

This is a thermometer for measuring the temperature of the air outside. 0°C is the freezing point of water.
Winter temperatures are towards the bottom of the thermometer and summer ones are towards the top.

–5°C is a cold winters day
25°C is a hot summers day
(Note that °C means degrees Celsius or degrees Centigrade)

Increasing temperatures
Use the diagram to understand these
a) The temperature is 5°C and rises by 10°C.
   The new temperature is 5 + 10 = 15°C.
b) The temperature is 0°C and rises by 10°C.
   The new temperature is 0 + 10 = 10°C.
c) The temperature is –5°C and rises by10°C.
   The new temperature is –5 + 10 = 5°C.
d) The temperature is –10°C and rises by 10°C.
   The new temperature is –10 + 10 = 0°C.
e) The temperature is –10°C and rises by 5°C.
   The new temperature is –10 + 5 = –5°C.
f) The temperature is –10°C and rises by 15°C.
   The new temperature is –10 + 15 = 5°C.

Exercise 1
Use the number line to help you.
1) 4°C rises by 7°C
2) 0°C rises by 8°C
3) –3°C rises by 5°C
4) –7°C rises by 10°C
5) –8°C rises by 8°C
6) –11°C rises by 21°C
7) –7°C rises by 3°C
8) –12°C rises by 9°C
9) –12°C rises by 15°C
10) –6°C rises by 1°C
11) –5 + 14
12) –10 + 14
13) –20 + 16
14) –6 + 8
15) –2 + 10
16) –7 + 4
17) –5 + 12
18) –6 + 12
19) –6 + 6
20) –8 + 7

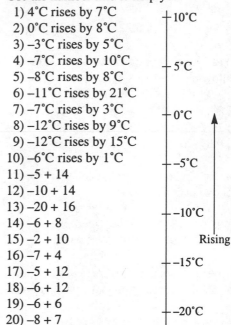

Falling temperatures
Again use the diagram to do these
a) The temperature is 15°C and falls by 10°C.
   The new temperature is 15 – 10 = 5°C.
b) The temperature is 10°C and falls by 10°C.
   The new temperature is 10 – 10 = 0°C.
c) The temperature is 5°C and falls by 10°C.
   The new temperature is 5 – 10 = –5°C.
d) The temperature is 0°C and falls by 10°C.
   The new temperature is 0 – 10 = –10°C.
e) The temperature is –5°C and falls by 10°C.
   The new temperature is –5 – 10 = –15°C.

Exercise 2
Use the number line to help you.

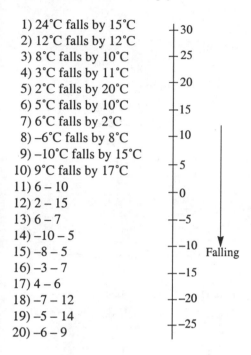

1) 24°C falls by 15°C
2) 12°C falls by 12°C
3) 8°C falls by 10°C
4) 3°C falls by 11°C
5) 2°C falls by 20°C
6) 5°C falls by 10°C
7) 6°C falls by 2°C
8) –6°C falls by 8°C
9) –10°C falls by 15°C
10) 9°C falls by 17°C
11) 6 – 10
12) 2 – 15
13) 6 – 7
14) –10 – 5
15) –8 – 5
16) –3 – 7
17) 4 – 6
18) –7 – 12
19) –5 – 14
20) –6 – 9

Exercise 3 - Mixed
1) On a summer day, the temperature is 22°C at midday and falls 8°C by midnight.
   What is the midnight temperature?
2) On a winters day the temperature is –4°C at midday and falls 8°C by midnight.
   What is the midnight temperature?
3) During the night the temperature falls to –10°C. If it then rises by 6°C, what is the new temperature?

4) On a day in summer the midday temperature is 22°C. If the midnight temperature is 12°C what is the temperature change?

5) On a day in winter the midday temperature is 2°C and the midnight temperature is –5°C. What is the fall in temperature?

6) If the temperature is 6°C and then falls by 12°C, what is the new temperature?

7) If the temperature is –7°C and rises by 10°C, what is the new temperature?

8) A bag of peas has a temperature of –18°C in the freezer. If they are heated up to 40°C, what is the change in temperature?

9) Copy this table and fill in the spaces.

Temperature of the peas in the freezer	Temperature of the peas outside of the freezer	Change of temperature
–8°C	40°C	
–5°C	5°C	
–12°C	6°C	
–6°C		12°C
–4°C		15°C
	10°C	15°C
	12°C	20°C
	8°C	15°C
–3°C		20°C
–7°C		13°C

For this section you need to know that 1000 grams (g) make 1 kilogram (kg)

So $\frac{1}{10}$ (0.1)kg = 100g

$\frac{1}{100}$ (0.01)kg = 10g

$\frac{1}{1000}$ (0.001)kg = 1g

This information can be used to convert from grams into kilograms and from kilograms into grams.

Changing grams into kilograms

Examples

Since 1g = 0.001kg

then 7g = 0.007kg

20g = 0.020 or 0.02kg

30g = 0.030 or 0.03kg

37g = 0.037kg

200g = 0.200 or 0.20 or 0.2kg

270g = 0.270 or 0.27kg

367g = 0.367kg

1236g = 1000 + 236g

= 1kg + 0.236kg = 1.236kg.

Exercise 1

Change each of the following into decimal kilograms.

1) 6g	2) 12g	3) 29g
4) 50g	5) 300g	6) 304g
7) 340g	8) 344g	9) 556g
10) 671g	11) 1126g	12) 2300g
13) 3450g	14) 5600g	15) 10,000g
16) 7141g	17) 5322g	18) 8643g

Changing from kilograms into grams

To do this, multiply by 1000. The best way to multiply by 1000 is to move the decimal point 3 places to the right.

Examples

1kg = 1000g

0.9kg = 900g

0.93kg = 930g

0.928kg = 928g

0.1kg = 100g

0.099kg = 99g

0.009kg = 9g

also 1.314kg = 1314g

Exercise 2

Change these decimal kilograms into grams.

1) 0.03kg	2) 0.006kg	3) 0.31kg
4) 0.375kg	5) 0.014kg	6) 0.187kg
7) 0.4kg	8) 0.86kg	9) 0.034kg
10) 1.371kg	11) 1.3kg	12) 1.67kg
13) 3.7kg	14) 16.4kg	15) 7.31kg
16) 10.4kg	17) 8.76kg	18) 9.815kg

Fractional problems involving weight

We can change grams into a fractional part of a kilogram by dividing it by 1000 (i.e. putting it over 1000)

Examples

$1 \text{ gram} = \frac{1}{1000} \text{ kg}$

$6 \text{ grams} = \frac{6}{1000} = \frac{3}{500} \text{ kg}$

(divide numerator and denominator by 2)

$17 \text{ grams} = \frac{17}{1000} \text{ kg}$

$200 \text{ grams} = \frac{200}{1000} = \frac{2}{10} = \frac{1}{5} \text{ kg}$

$1300 \text{ grams} = \frac{1300}{1000} = \frac{13}{10} = 1\frac{3}{10} \text{ kg}$

$\frac{1}{4} \text{ kg} = \frac{1}{4} \times 1000 = \frac{1000}{4} = 250\text{g}$

$\frac{7}{10} \text{ kg} = \frac{7}{10} \times 1000 = \frac{7000}{10} = \frac{700}{1} = 700\text{g}$

$1\frac{3}{10} \text{ kg} = 1\frac{3}{10} \times 1000 = 1000 + \frac{3000}{10}$

$$= 1000\text{g} + 300\text{g} = 1300\text{g}$$

(See page 33)

Exercise 3

Change the following grams into fractions of a kilogram

1) 27g
2) 53g
3) 187g
4) 361g
5) 500g
6) 250g
7) 100g
8) 370g
9) 850g
10) 1500g
11) 2250g
12) 3400g
13) 1650g
14) 2027g
15) 3510g
16) 5400g
17) 8350g
18) 9310g

Changing fractions of kilograms into grams

This is done by multiplying by 1000 (see page 32)

Examples

$\frac{1}{2} \text{ kg} = \frac{1}{2} \times 1000 = \frac{1000}{2} = \frac{500}{1} = 500\text{g}$

Exercise 4

Change the following kilograms into grams.

1) $\frac{3}{4}$ kg
2) $\frac{4}{5}$ kg
3) $\frac{2}{5}$ kg
4) $\frac{1}{10}$ kg
5) $1\frac{1}{2}$ kg
6) $2\frac{1}{4}$ kg
7) $3\frac{3}{10}$ kg
8) $3\frac{3}{4}$ kg
9) $3\frac{1}{20}$ kg
10) $4\frac{1}{5}$ kg
11) $\frac{9}{10}$ kg
12) $1\frac{17}{100}$ kg
13) $6\frac{1}{8}$ kg
14) $\frac{7}{20}$ kg
15) $\frac{3}{50}$ kg
16) $7\frac{3}{20}$ kg
17) $9\frac{3}{5}$ kg
18) $7\frac{1}{8}$ kg

Capacity

Millilitres and Litres

The majority of capacity measurements are in millilitres and litres.

For this section you need to know that 1000 millilitres (ml) make 1 litre (L)

so $100ml = \frac{1}{10}$ L or 0.1L

$10ml = \frac{1}{100}$ L or 0.01L

$1ml = \frac{1}{1000}$ L or 0.001L

From this list it is possible to change other amounts from millilitres into litres.

$$100ml = 0.1L$$
$$300ml = 0.3L$$
$$500ml = 0.5L$$
and so on.
$$10ml = 0.01L$$
$$40ml = 0.04L$$
$$80ml = 0.08L$$
and so on
$$1ml = 0.001L$$
$$6ml = 0.006L$$
$$9ml = 0.009L$$
and so on

By using this information it is possible to change other values

$$120ml = 100ml + 20ml$$
$$= 0.1 + 0.02 = 0.12L$$

This could be done by dividing by 1000

$$120ml = 120.0ml$$
$$120.0 \div 1000 = 0.1200L$$
(move the d.p three places to the left)
$$= 0.12L$$
(end zeros are not needed)

Similarly
$356ml = 356 \div 1000 = 0.356$Litres
$3148ml = 3148 \div 1000 = 3.148L$
$4500ml = 4500 \div 1000 = 4.500L = 4.5L$
$6080ml = 6080 \div 1000 = 6.080L = 6.08L$

Exercise 1

Change the following millilitres into Litres

1) 800ml	2) 27ml
3) 132ml	4) 70ml
5) 6ml	6) 450ml
7) 6,142ml	8) 4,100ml
9) 62ml	10) 127ml
11) 841ml	12) 1250ml
13)1006ml	14) 12,200ml
15) 3105ml	16) 4,060ml
17) 15,004ml	18) 4810ml

Changing from Litres into millilitres

This is done by multiplying by 1000.

Examples

1) $\qquad 2.6L = 2.6 \times 1000$
$\qquad\qquad = 2600.$ or 2600ml
(by moving the decimal point to the right)

2) $0.32L = 0.32 \times 1000 = 320ml$

3) $0.002L = 0.002 \times 1000ml = 2ml$

Exercise 2

Change the following into millilitres

1) 0.7L	2) 0.45L	3) 0.76L
4) 0.934L	5) 0.631L	6) 0.701L
7) 1.6L	8) 3.74L	9) 8.9L
10) 5.61L	11) 7.32L	12) 4.817L
13) 6.931L	14) 4.702L	15) 6.005L
16) 0.002L	17) 0.009L	18) 0.093L
19) 0.040L	20) 0.050L	21) 0.005L

Fractional problems involving capacity

To change millilitres into fractional parts of a litre, divide by 1000. (i.e. put over 1000 and cancel down)

$1ml = \frac{1}{1000}$ L

$3ml = \frac{3}{1000}$ L

$19ml = \frac{19}{1000}$ L

$30ml = \frac{30}{1000} = \frac{3}{100}L$

$400ml = \frac{400}{1000} = \frac{4}{10} = \frac{2}{5}L$

$2800ml = \frac{2800}{1000} = \frac{28}{10} = \frac{14}{5} = 2\frac{4}{5}L$

Exercise 3
Change the following millilitres into fractions of litres.

1) 7ml	2) 37ml	3) 149ml
4) 1397ml	5) 8ml	6) 45ml
7) 250ml	8) 2500ml	9) 50ml
10) 75ml	11) 400ml	12) 820ml
13) 940ml	14) 1050ml	15) 2050ml

Changing fractions of Litres into millilitres

This is done by multiplying by 1000.

Examples

1) $\qquad \frac{3}{4}L = \frac{3}{4} \times 1000$

$= \frac{3000}{4} = \frac{1500}{2} = \frac{750}{1} = 750ml$

2) $\quad \frac{3}{10}L = \frac{3}{10} \times 1000 = \frac{3000}{10} = 300ml$

3) $\qquad 1\frac{3}{8}L = 1\frac{3}{8} \times 1000$

$= 1000 + \frac{3000}{8} = 1000 + 375 = 1375ml$

(note: the cancelling down of $\frac{3000}{8}$ could be done in easy stages by dividing by 2 each time

i.e. $\frac{3000}{8} = \frac{1500}{4} = \frac{750}{2} = \frac{375}{1} = 375ml)$

Exercise 4
Change each of the following into millilitres

1) $\frac{1}{2}L$ 2) $\frac{7}{10}L$ 3) $\frac{1}{5}L$ 4) $\frac{3}{5}L$

5) $2\frac{3}{4}L$ 6) $3\frac{1}{2}L$ 7) $\frac{1}{40}L$ 8) $\frac{3}{20}L$

9) $1\frac{1}{20}L$ 10) $1\frac{4}{25}L$ 11) $3\frac{2}{5}$ 12) $2\frac{1}{25}$

13) $3\frac{9}{25}$ 14) $\frac{5}{8}L$ 15) $3\frac{1}{8}L$ 16) $5\frac{3}{25}L$

Centilitres and Litres
Some capacity measurements are in centilitres.

There are 100 centilitres (cl) in 1 litre (L)

So 10 cl $= \frac{1}{10}$ L or 0.1 L

1cl $= \frac{1}{100}$ or 0.01 L

Use this information to do each of the following questions.

Exercise 5
1) Change into litres
a) 20cl   b) 73cl   c) 120cl
d) 210 cl   e) 350cl   f) 1,200cl
2) Change into centilitres
a) 0.3L   b) 0.75L   c) 1.3L
d) 5.4L   e) 10.3L   f) 6.7lL
3) Change into fractions of litres
a) 4cl   b) 53cl   c) 15cl
d) 150cl   e) 220cl   f) 500cl
4) Change each of the following into centilitres
a) $\frac{1}{2}L$ b) $\frac{1}{4}$ L   c) $\frac{3}{10}$
d) $\frac{7}{20}$ e) $1\frac{1}{4}L$ f) $3\frac{1}{8}$

Length

For this section you need to know that
10 millimetres (mm) make 1cm
100 centimetres (cm) make 1 metre (m)
or 1000mm make 1m
1000m make 1 kilometre (km)

Metres and centimetres
100 centimetres (cm) make 1 metre(m)

so 1cm = 0.01m or $\frac{1}{100}$ m

10cm = 0.1m or $\frac{10}{100}$ = $\frac{1}{10}$ m

7cm = 0.07m or $\frac{7}{100}$ m

50cm = 0.50m or 0.5m or $\frac{50}{100}$ m = $\frac{1}{2}$ m

206cm = 2.06m or $\frac{206}{100}$ = $\frac{103}{50}$ = $2\frac{3}{50}$ m

Exercise 1
Change the following centimetres into (a) decimal metres and (b) fractional metres.

1) 9cm	2) 13cm	3) 47cm
4) 2cm	5) 26cm	6) 82cm
7) 4cm	8) 25cm	9) 96cm
10) 15cm	11) 55cm	12) 85cm
13) 140cm	14) 260cm	15) 580cm
16) 350cm	17) 425cm	18) 544cm

Examples
To change from m into cm multiply by 100.
1) 6.3m = 6.3 × 100 = 630. or 630cm
2) 0.04m = 0.04 × 100 = 4. or 4cm
3) 0.42m = 0.42 × 100 = 42. or 42cm
4) $\frac{3}{10}$ m = $\frac{3}{10}$ × 100 = $\frac{300}{10}$ = 30cm
5) $\frac{3}{5}$ m = $\frac{3}{5}$ × 100 = $\frac{300}{5}$ = 60cm
6) $2\frac{3}{10}$ m = $2\frac{3}{10}$ × 100 = 200 + $\frac{300}{10}$
  = 200 + 30 = 230cm
7) $4\frac{7}{20}$ m = $4\frac{7}{20}$ × 100 = 400 + $\frac{700}{20}$
  = 400 + $\frac{70}{2}$ = 400 + 35 = 435cm
(see page 33 for this type of multiplication)

Exercise 2
Change the following into centimetres

1) 0.08m	2) 0.45m	3) 0.80m
4) 1.76m	5) 1.94m	6) 2.37m
7) 5.96m	8) 14.68m	9) 14.04m
10) $3\frac{1}{2}$ m	11) $4\frac{1}{4}$ m	12) $3\frac{3}{10}$ m
13) $6\frac{2}{5}$ m	14) $4\frac{3}{20}$ m	15) $5\frac{17}{25}$ m
16) $8\frac{8}{25}$ m	17) $10\frac{4}{5}$ m	18) $9\frac{3}{4}$ m

Metres, centimetres and millimetres
Exercise 3
1) Change from centimetres into millimetres;

a) 0.7cm	b) 2cm	c) 3.4cm
d) 8cm	e) 12cm	f) 23.4cm
g) $\frac{1}{2}$ cm	h) $\frac{1}{4}$ cm	i) $1\frac{1}{2}$

2) Change from millimetres into centimetres;

a) 30mm	b) 45mm	c) 9mm
d) 84mm	e) 105mm	f) 450mm

3) Change from metres into millimetres;

a) 1.5m	b) 0.5m	c) 0.3m
d) 0.09m	e) 0.43m	f) 0.32.
g) $2\frac{1}{2}$ m	h) $\frac{1}{4}$ m	i) $\frac{1}{10}$ m

4) Change from millimetres into metres;

a) 2000mm	b) 3,500mm	c) 750mm
d) 300mm	e) 90mm	f) 64mm

Kilometres and metres
Exercise 4
1) Change from km into m by multiplying.

a) 0.5km	b) $\frac{1}{4}$ km	c) 3.1km
d) $2\frac{1}{2}$ km	e) 0.07km	f) 1.35km

2) Change from m into km by dividing

a) 1500m	b) 200m	c) 3250
d) 190m	e) 1450	f) 79m

Most monetary systems throughout the world use a decimal system where 100 small units make one large unit. This means that they all work in the same way. The British system is based on 100 pennies making one pound.

i.e. 100p = £1

so 6p = £0.06

20p = £0.20 (notice that in the money system this is not called £0.2 but £0.20)

67p = £0.67

127p = £1.27

500p = £5 or £5.00 but <u>never</u> £5.0

Exercise 1

Change these into pounds

1) 9p	2) 20p	3) 35p
4) 50p	5) 84p	6)127p
7) 294p	8) 803p	9) 1001p
10) 1600p	11) 2714p	12) 6141p
13) 3740p	14)8162p	15) 19421p

Exercise 2

Change these into pence

1) £1.84	2) £2.45	3) £8.30
4) £6.04	5) £3.24	6) £0.23
7) £0.50	8) £3.08	9) £10.20
10) £1.97	11) £2.31	12) £0.03
13) £5.43	14) £0.45	15) £10.37

Adding together money

This must be done by writing all the values down in the same way

Example 1

£1.24 + £3.21 + 67p

In order to do this, all the values must be written down in the same form.

i.e.
$$
\begin{array}{rr}
£ \ p & p \\
1.24 & 124 \\
3.21 \quad \text{or} & 321 \\
0.67 & \underline{67} \\
\underline{5.12} & 512 \\
1\ 1 & 1\ 1
\end{array}
$$

Exercise 3

Add together each of the following amounts of money.

1) £3.89 + £4.23 + £6.89

2) £5.35 + £6.89 + £3.90

3) 27p + 67p + 45p

4) 45p + 99p + 67p

5) £2.78 + £2.98 + 67p

6) £1.96 + £6.65 + 76p

7) £9.67 + £0.87 + 43p

8) £13.23 + 63p + 84p + £4.76

9) £11.76 + 54p + £0.87 + £32.87

10) £13.56 + £7.74 + 76p + 15p

11) 47p + 38p + £1.63 + £0.42

12) £8.64 + £3.96 + £0.32 + 89p

The layout for subtraction should be done in the same way.

Example 2

£3.34 − 67p

$$
\begin{array}{rr}
\overset{2}{\cancel{3}}.\overset{1}{\cancel{3}}\overset{2}{\cancel{4}} & \overset{2}{\cancel{3}}\overset{1}{\cancel{3}}\overset{2}{\cancel{4}} \\
-0.67 \quad \text{or} & -067 \\
\underline{2.67} & \underline{267} \\
£2.67 & 267p
\end{array}
$$

(see pages 12 and 39)

Exercise 4

Subtract the following.

1) 156p − 43p	2) 253p − 41p
3) 73p − 57p	4) 134p − 99p
5) £1.67 − £1.22	6) £3.45 − £2.21
7) £1.73 − £1.27	8) £5.47 − £3.69
9) £1.34 − 67p	10) £3.67 − 86p
11) £6.52 − £3.76	12) £2.73 − 39p
13) £12.27 − 59p	14) £6.43 − £2.79

Area of a Rectangle

Area is a measure of how much surface something covers. For example, look at the diagram below. It is the plan of a lawn.

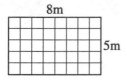

Each side of it has been marked off at one metre intervals. Each of the squares measures 1 metre by 1 metre. This is called a square metre.

If you count up the number of squares on the large diagram you will find that there are 40. So this lawn measures 40 square metres. Instead of marking out the diagram and counting the squares, the area can be calculated by multiplying the 8 by the 5
$$\text{i.e. } 8 \times 5 = 40$$
so multiplying the lengths of the two sides together gives the area.

Look at the areas of these rectangles.

Example 1

Area is $5 \times 4 = 20$ square metres

Example 2

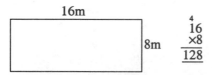

Area is $16 \times 8 = 128$ square metres

With decimals

Example 3

Area is 4.5×1.5
$= 6.75$ square centimetres

Example 4

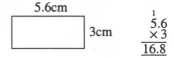

Area is 16.8 sq. cm.

With fractions

Example 5

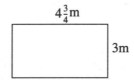

$$\text{Area} = 4\tfrac{3}{4} \times 3 = \tfrac{19}{4} \times \tfrac{3}{1} = \tfrac{57}{4} = 14\tfrac{1}{4} \text{ sq. m.}$$

Example 6

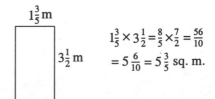

$$1\tfrac{3}{5} \times 3\tfrac{1}{2} = \tfrac{8}{5} \times \tfrac{7}{2} = \tfrac{56}{10}$$
$$= 5\tfrac{6}{10} = 5\tfrac{3}{5} \text{ sq. m.}$$

Exercise 1
Calculate the areas of each of these rectangles.

1)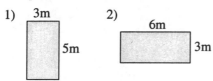
3m
5m

2)
6m
3m

3)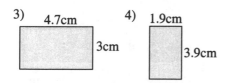
4.7cm
3cm

4) 1.9cm
3.9cm

5)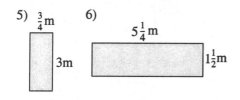
$\frac{3}{4}$m
3m

6)
$5\frac{1}{4}$m
$1\frac{1}{2}$m

7) 6cm by 12cm   8) 8.3cm by 6cm
9) 4.7cm by 4cm   10) 3.2cm by 1.2cm
11) 8.6cm by 2.1cm   12) 4.3cm by 2.6cm
13) $3\frac{1}{2}$ cm by 3cm   14) $4\frac{1}{4}$ cm by $\frac{1}{2}$ cm

Shapes made up of more than one rectangle

In such a case calculate the area of each rectangle and then add them together.

Example

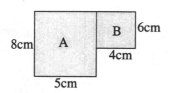
8cm
A
B
6cm
4cm
5cm

Area of rectangle A = 8 × 5 = 40 sq cm
Area of rectangle B = 6 × 4 = 24 sq cm

Area of the whole shape = 40 + 24
= 64 sq cm

Exercise 2
Calculate the areas of each of the following shapes by first splitting them up into smaller rectangles.

1)
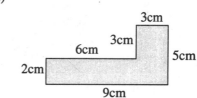
4cm
3cm
5cm
4cm
7cm

2)
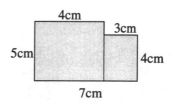
3cm
3cm
6cm
5cm
2cm
9cm

3)
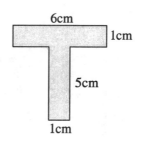
6cm
1cm
5cm
1cm

4)
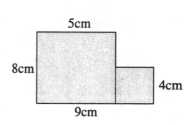
5cm
8cm
4cm
9cm

67

5)

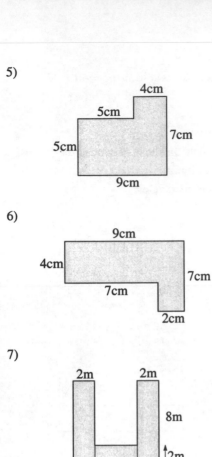

4cm
5cm
5cm
7cm
9cm

10)

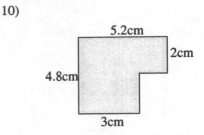

5.2cm
2cm
4.8cm
3cm

6)

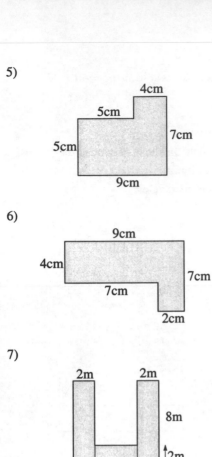

9cm
4cm
7cm
7cm
2cm

11)

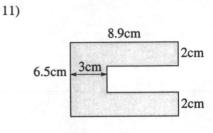

8.9cm
2cm
6.5cm   3cm
2cm

7)

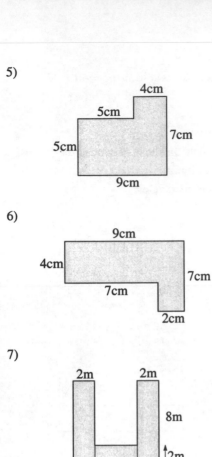

2m   2m
8m
2m
8m

12)

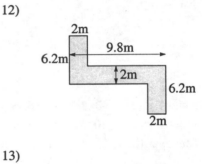

2m
6.2m   9.8m
2m
6.2m
2m

8)

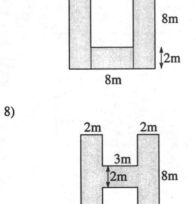

2m   2m
3m
2m   8m

13)

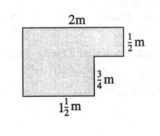

2m
$\frac{1}{2}$ m
$\frac{3}{4}$ m
$1\frac{1}{2}$ m

9)

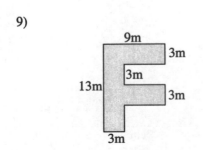

9m
3m
3m
13m
3m
3m

14)

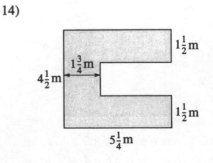

$1\frac{1}{2}$ m
$1\frac{3}{4}$ m
$4\frac{1}{2}$ m
$1\frac{1}{2}$ m
$5\frac{1}{4}$ m

Volume of a Cuboid

A <u>Cuboid</u> is a box shaped object which has rectangular sides.

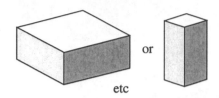

or

etc

A <u>cube</u> is a box shaped object which has square sides. It is a special type of cuboid.

We measure the <u>volume</u> of a cuboid by calculating how much space there is inside of it. We do this by counting up the number of 1 centimetre cubes it has.

1cm

1cm   1cm

Consider this shape

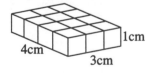

1cm

4cm

3cm

It is a cuboid which measures 4cm by 3cm by 1cm. If you count up the number of 1 centimetre cubes in it you will see that there are 12. We say that the shape has a volume of 12 cubic centimetres (or c.c.)

Now look at this shape

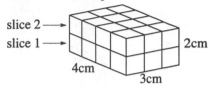

slice 2

slice 1

2cm

4cm

3cm

It is made up of two slices of the first shape.

Its volume is therefore

2 × the volume of the first shape.

i.e. 24 cubic centimetres (c.c.)

Without the centimetre cubes drawn, this cuboid looks like this

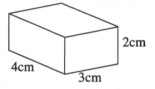

2cm

4cm

3cm

To calculate its volume, first multiply the 4 by the 3 to calculate the number of centimetres cubes in a slice.

Then multiply by the number of slices (2)

i.e. $4 \times 3 \times 2 = 12 \times 2$

$= 24$ c.c.

So the rule for calculating the volume of a cuboid is to multiply together the **three dimensions.**

We say

Volume = length × width × height

It is worth noting that the numbers can be multiplied together in any order.

i.e $4 \times 3 \times 2 = 24$

$3 \times 4 \times 2 = 24$

$3 \times 2 \times 4 = 24$

$2 \times 4 \times 3 = 24$

and so on

Exercise

Calculate the volume of each of the
following cuboids.

1)

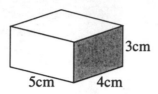

3cm
5cm   4cm

2)

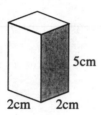

5cm
2cm   2cm

3)

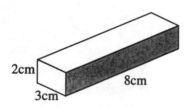

2cm
3cm   8cm

4)

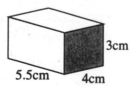

3cm
5.5cm   4cm

5)

2cm
4cm   6.8cm

6)

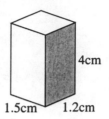

4cm
1.5cm   1.2cm

7) 3cm by 4cm by 11cm
8) 12cm by 6cm by 9cm
9) 4.3cm by 4.2cm by 7cm
10) 2.8cm by 4.1cm by 6cm

(See also page 69 on volume and page 62 on capacity.)

Consider a centimetre cube.

The amount of space this takes up is called 1 cubic centimetre (c.c.). If we were to think of this as a box, then the amount of liquid it will hold is 1 millilitre.

So a volume of 1 cubic centimetre will hold 1 millimetre of liquid (or gas etc)

Example 1

What is the capacity of this cuboid.

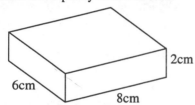

Volume = 6 × 8 × 2

= 48 × 2

= 96 cc

So its capacity is 96 millilitres

Example 2

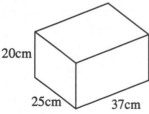

Volume = 20 × 25 × 37

= 500 × 37

= 18500 c.c.

So its capacity is 18,500 millilitres or 18.5 litres

(remember that 1000ml = 1L)

Exercise

Calculate the capacity of each of these boxes. Give your answer in either millilitres or litres, whichever is the most appropriate.

1)

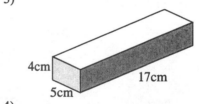

2)

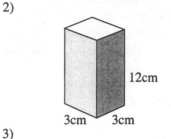

3)

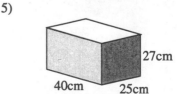

4)

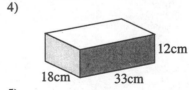

5)

6) 8cm by 12cm by 16cm

7) 14cm by 25cm by 50cm

8) 47cm by 40cm by 23cm

9) 7.3cm by 18cm by 20cm

10) 5.2cm by 3.5cm by 9cm

The 12 hour clock

On the 12 hour clock, times between 12 o'clock midnight, and 12 o'clock midday (noon) are called a.m. (ante meridiem) and times between 12 o'clock midday through to 12 o'clock midnight are called p.m. (post meridiem).

So one o'clock at night is called 1:00 a.m. and one o'clock in the afternoon is called 1:00 p.m.

12 o'clock midnight is called 12:00 p.m.
1 minute past midnight is called 12:01 a.m.

12 o'clock midday is called 12:00 a.m.
1 minute past midday is called 12:01 p.m.

24 hour clock

On the 24 hour clock, times begin immediately after midnight.

Midnight is either 24:00 of the old day or 00:00 of the new day.
One minute past midnight is 00:01

12 o'clock midday is 12:00
1:00 p.m. is 13:00
6:00 p.m. is 18:00
and so on up to 24:00

Here are some comparisons

12 hour clock	24 hour clock
12:30 a.m.	00:30
1:00 a.m.	01:00
3:15 a.m.	03:15
7:45 a.m.	07:45
12:00 a.m.	12:00
6:05 p.m.	18:05
7:35 p.m	19:35
12:00 p.m.	24:00 / 00:00

Exercise 1
Say what these times are on the 24 hour clock
1) 7:00 a.m.   2) 7:20 a.m.
3) 3:45 a.m.   4) 9:25 p.m.
5) 12:10 a.m.   6) 12:10 p.m.
7) $\frac{1}{4}$ to 4 in the afternoon
8) Half past six in the morning
9) 25 minutes to 3 in the afternoon
10) 20 minutes to 11 in the morning
11) six thirty in the morning
12) $\frac{1}{4}$ to 12 at night
13) $\frac{1}{4}$ past 12 at night
14) 5 minutes to 2 in the afternoon

Time intervals
To find how long it is between two times, do it by 'counting on'.

Example 1
What is the time interval between 2:05 and 3:15?
By counting on
    2:05 to 3:00 is 55 minutes
    3:00 to 3:15 is 15 minutes
So the time interval is
    55 minutes + 15 minutes
 = 70 minutes = 1 hour and 10 minutes

Note. Time is not written in the decimal form. For that there would have to be 10 or 100 minutes to the hour. It is therefore not possible to use the 'decimal' methods of addition and subtraction.

Example 2
What is the time interval between 12:27 p.m. and 3:15 p.m?
By counting on
    12:27 to 12:30 is 3 minutes
    12:30 to 1:00 is 30 minutes
    1:00 to 3:15 is 2 hours 15 minutes

So the time interval is
    3 mins + 30 mins + 2 hrs 15mins
    = 2 hours 48 minutes

Exercise 2
Do these in stages by counting on.
1) Find the time interval between these times.
a) 1:00 a.m. and 6:30 a.m.
b) 1:15 p.m. and 2:45 p.m.
c) 12:30 and 14:15
d) 06:20 and 07:15
e) 12:30 p.m. and 2:15 p.m.
f) 07:15 and 12:05
g) 23:30 and 00:00
h) 23:00 and 01:30
i) 6:30 a.m. and 11:15 a.m.
j) 9:14 a.m. and 12:15 p.m.
2) John leaves home at 8:15. He arrives at work at 8:44. How long does this take?
3) Elizabeth leaves home at 10 minutes past 8. She arrives at work at a quarter to 9. How long does she take?
4) Jane and Sarah go on a shopping trip. They leave home at 9:15 and arrive back at $\frac{1}{4}$ to 12. How long does the trip take?
5) Ann and David watch a football match on a Saturday afternoon. They leave home at 14:05 and arrive back at 18:00. How long have they been away from home?
6) Mary sits a mathematics examination. If it begins at 9:30 and finishes at 11:20, how long does it last?
7) Saturday sport on television begins at 12:30 p.m. and ends at 5:05 p.m. For how long does the programme last?

Adding on time.
Remember that there are 60 minutes in 1 hour.

Example 2
A T.V. programme begins at 7:55 p.m. and lasts for 1 hour 50 minutes. At what time does it finish?

Starting at 7:55
Step 1. add on the 1 hour to get 8:55
Step 2. add on the 50 minutes to the 55 minutes to give 105 minutes.
So the time will now be
    8 hours + 105 minutes
But 105 minutes is 1 hour 45 minutes.
So the time will be
    8 hours + 1 hour + 45 minutes
        or 9:45 p.m.

Example 4
What will the time be 2 hours 45 minutes after 08:50?

08:50 + 2 hours is 10:50
45mins + 50mins = 95mins or 1hr 35 mins.
So 10:50 + 45mins = 11:35

Exercise 3
1) What will the time be 2hrs 30mins after 12:45?
2) What will the time be 1hrs 55mins after 11:30 a.m?
3) What will the time be 3hrs 15mins after 01:40?
4) What will the time be 1hr 10mins after 03:35?
5) What will the time be 3hrs 15mins after 4:40 p.m?
6) What will the time be 2hrs 50mins after 6:53 p.m?
7) What will the time be 5hrs 6mins after 7:19 a.m?
8) What will the time be 2hrs 27mins after 09:50?
9) What will the time be 3hrs 16mins after 23:57?
10) What will the time be 4hrs 30mins after 23:45?

There are many types of tables used to show information. Here are just a sample.

Example 1
In order to save space, some tables do not have all the information written in, but expect the user to fill in the blanks.
Below is shown a part of a bus timetable. It gives some of the departure times from the Town Hall and Apple Way. But since some of the times are every 30 minutes, these have been left out. You have to work these out yourself.

Town Hall	0800	0815	0830	0845	0900	Then every 30 minutes until	1800	1900
Apple Way	0822	0837	0852	0907	0922		1822	1922

Here are some of the important points.
a) The first bus of the day is the 0800 from the Town Hall and the last bus is at 1900.
b) Each bus takes 22 minutes to get from the Town Hall to Apple Way.
c) After 0900 the busses run at 30 minute intervals, until 1800. So the next bus after 0900 is at 0930, the next is at 1000, the next is at 1030 and so on until 1800.
Questions
a) At what time does the 0815 from the Town Hall arrive at Apple Way?
b) At what time will the 0930 from the Town Hall arrive at Apple Way?
c) How long will the 1200 from the Town Hall take to get to Apple Way?
d) If the 1630 from the Town Hall is late by 16 minutes because of a traffic hold up, at what time will it arrive at Apple Way?

Example 2
Information is selected from the next type of table by reading across the top row and down the left hand column. The information required is then shown within the table. For example, the highlighted box shows the cost of a 1 week holiday in a 4 star hotel beginning between 1st July and 31st August.

Type of accommodation		2 star	3 star	4 star	5 star
Starting date on or between	20 Mar - 30 Apr	849	889	999	1109
	01 May - 30 Jun	959	965	1119	1229
	01 Jul - 31 Aug	1039	1099	1209	1319
	01 Sep - 31 Oct	969	1019	1129	1239
	01 Nov - 12 Dec	859	899	1009	1119
	13 Dec - 24 Dec	1059	1119	1229	1339
	25 Dec - 31 Dec	859	899	1009	1119

Questions
a) What is the cost of a holiday for 1 person in a 5 star hotel starting on 2nd July?
b) Calculate the cost of a holiday for 2 people in a 4 star hotel starting on 2nd December.
c) Calculate the cost of a holiday for a family of 4 in a 2 star hotel starting on 17th August.

Example 3   Distance Tables

	Birmingham	Cardiff	Edinburgh	Glasgow	London	Manchester	Newcastle
Cardiff	99						
Edinburgh	289	373					
Glasgow	290	370	45				
London	113	154	386	403			
Manchester	81	172	213	214	189		
Newcastle	205	298	105	142	281	132	
Swansea	125	45	380	381	192	183	314

This table shows the distances between some cities in Britain.
The distance between London and Cardiff is highlighted as 154 miles.
Questions
a) What is the distance between Swansea and Glasgow?
b) What is the distance between Newcastle and London?
c) Which towns are the closest?
d) Which towns are furthest from each other?

Mean (Average)

Example 1

Consider the diagram below showing three bottles containing 72ml, 87ml and 81ml of water.

72ml   87ml   81ml

Now pour the water from one bottle to another until they each have the same amount of water in them.

80ml   80ml   80ml

80ml is the mean amount of water in the three bottles.

Note that 'Mean' is the correct word to describe this. However 'Average' is more commonly used. From now on I will use 'average'

To calculate the average amount of water in the three bottles, add together all the water then divide by 3

Average

$$= \frac{72 + 87 + 81}{3} \longleftarrow \text{Divide the top by the bottom}$$

$$= \frac{240}{3} = 80ml \qquad \frac{240}{3} \text{ means } 240 \div 3$$

Example 2

The ages of four friends are 27, 25, 29 and 33. What is their average age?

$$\text{Average age} = \frac{27 + 25 + 29 + 33}{4}$$

$$= \frac{114}{4}$$

$$= 28.5 \text{ years or 28 years 6 months}$$

Exercise 1

Calculate the average of each of the following groups of numbers
1) 4, 8, 6, 7, 5.
2) 11, 12, 15, 14.
3) 14, 20, 21, 28, 32.
4) 20, 25, 31, 42.
5) 16, 24, 18, 19, 23.
6) 20, 32, 28, 43, 52, 65.
7) Four friends go out for a meal. They decide to share the total cost equally. If the four meals cost £9.40, £8.70, £10.20 and £9.50, how much do they each pay?

Average Speed
(miles per hour or kilometres per hour)

Example 3

Imagine a car travelling from Glasgow to London, a distance of 400 miles. The car would be continually changing speed according to the road conditions. It might have to go slowly through a town centre and stop at traffic lights. It will travel at a higher speed down the motorway.

The average speed for the journey will even out all these differences of speed and give a value which represents the whole journey. If the journey is carried out in 8 hours, the average speed is

$$400 \div 8 = 50 \text{ miles per hour (mph)}$$

i.e. if the car travelled the 400 miles at a constant speed, that speed would be 50mph.

If the journey was carried out in 10 hours, then the average speed would be

$$400 \div 10 = 40mph$$

Example 2

A train travels a distance of 210 kilometres between two towns. The total time taken is 3 hours. What is its average speed?

$$\text{Average speed} = 210 \div 3$$

$$= 70 \text{ kilometres per hour (kph)}$$

Exercise 2

1) The distance between two towns is 120 miles. It takes two hours for a train to travel between the towns. What is the train's average speed?

2) A long distance runner covers 24 miles in 3 hours. What is his average speed?

3) Jane goes on a walking tour. She travels a distance of 20 miles in 8 hours. What is her average speed?

4) To get from town A to town B, a car travels 20 miles in 1 hour, a further 40 miles in 1 hour and the final 92 miles in 2 hours. What is its average speed?

5) An aeroplane travels a distance of 1,400 kilometres in $3\frac{1}{2}$ hours.
a) If it continued at this speed, how far would it travel in 7 hours?
b) What is its average speed?

6) A cyclist travels 40 miles in $2\frac{1}{2}$ hours. What is her average speed?

Fuel consumption

In the same way that average speed is calculated, average fuel consumption can be calculated.

Example 5
Suppose a car travels 140 miles and uses up 4 gallons of petrol.
Average fuel consumption = 140 ÷ 4
= 35 miles per gallon
i.e. on average, the car travels 35 miles on one gallon of petrol

Example 6
A car travels a distance of 160 kilometres and uses up 20 litres of petrol. What is its average fuel consumption?
Average fuel consumption = 160 ÷ 20
= 8 km per litre.

Exercise 3

1) A car travels 300 miles and uses up 8 gallons of petrol. What is its average fuel consumption?

2) A car travels 230 kilometres and uses 30 litres of fuel. What is its average fuel consumption?

3) A car travels 170 kilometres and uses 20 litres of petrol. What is its average fuel consumption?

4) What is the average fuel consumption of a car which travels 250 miles and uses 8 gallons of petrol?

Recap Test 4 - Measurement

1) Calculate
a) –3 + 4   b) –5 +2   c) 4 –7
d) 0 – 6   e) 12 – 15   f) 10 – 12

2) The daytime temperature is 6°C. If the night time temperature is –8°C, what is the drop in temperature?

3) Change into kilograms
a) 2500g   b) 1250g   c) 645g   d) 27g

4) Change into grams
a) 1.5kg   b) 0.58kg
c) 0.014kg   d) 0.003kg
e) $\frac{1}{2}$ kg   f) $\frac{3}{5}$ kg   g) $1\frac{1}{20}$ kg   h) $2\frac{3}{4}$ kg

5) Change into fractions of kg
a) 250g   b) 600g   c) 1,400g   d) 2450g

6) Change into decimal litres
a) 400ml   b) 850ml   c) 60ml
d) 1800ml   e) 80cl   f) 150cl
g) 300cl   h) 75cl

7) Change into millilitres
a) 3litres   b) 1.47litres   c) 0.03litres

8) Change into centilitres
a) 2.5L   b) 1.36L   c) 0.08L

9) Change into metres and centimetres
a) 3.4 metres   b) 8.35 metres

10) Change into millimetres
a) 0.3 metres   b) 1.4metres   c) 8cm
d) $\frac{1}{2}$ metre   e) $\frac{1}{2}$ cm   f) $\frac{3}{4}$ cm

11) Change into pence
a) £1.37   b) £0.42   c) £15.43

12) Change into pounds and pence
a) 240p   b) 16p   c) 2568p

13) Add together £1.47, £3.84, £0.43 and 84p

14) Subtract 89p from £6.42

15) Calculate the areas of these shapes
a)
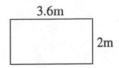

b)
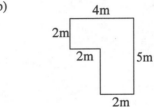

c)
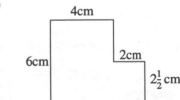

16) Calculate the volumes of these cuboids
a)
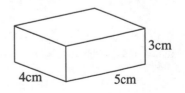

b)

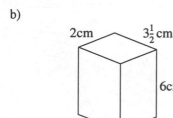

17) What is the relationship between a cubic centimetre and a millilitre?

18) Calculate the capacity, in ml, cl or litres, of each of the following cuboids.
a)

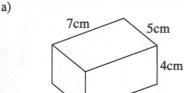

b)

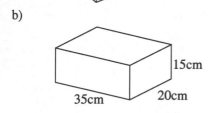

19) Write down the following times in the 24 hour system
a) 3:30am   b) 3:30pm
c) 12:00 midnight

20) Write down the following times in the 12 hour system
a) 00:15   b) 12:15   c) 17:24

21) A T.V. programme begins at 9:30pm and finishes at a quarter to 11. How long does it last?

22) Another T.V. programme begins at 7:20 and lasts for 1 hour 35 minutes. At what time will it finish?

23) On the bus timetable on page 74, at what time will the 11:30 bus from the Town Hall arrive at Apple Way?

24) On the distance table on page 74, what is the distance between Manchester and Newcastle?

25) On the holiday price table, on page 74, what is the cost of a holiday for two people in a three star hotel beginning on 27th September?

26) What is the average age of 5 people who are 26, 30, 19, 27 and 23?

27) What is the average speed of a train that travels a distance of 330 miles in 6 hours?

28) What is the average fuel consumption of a car which uses up 8 litres when travelling 60 miles?

Why use a calculator?

Nearly every calculation can be carried out quicker than by pencil and paper. Whether you use a calculator depends on the level of your skill. If you can carry out the calculation quite easily in your head or on paper then you should do it this way. It will exercise your brain and ensure that you don't forget the skills involved. However when the figures become more difficult then is the time to use the calculator.

Addition and subtraction

Addition and Subtraction is carried out using the $\boxed{+}$, $\boxed{-}$ and $\boxed{=}$ buttons

Example 1
$$3 + 4$$

$\boxed{AC}$ $\boxed{3}$ $\boxed{+}$ $\boxed{4}$ $\boxed{=}$ 7

Press these in order   This is the answer

Example 2
$$4.1 + 3.73$$

$\boxed{AC}$ $\boxed{4}$ $\boxed{\cdot}$ $\boxed{1}$ $\boxed{+}$

$\boxed{3}$ $\boxed{\cdot}$ $\boxed{7}$ $\boxed{3}$ $\boxed{=}$ 7·83

Note.
Before you do any calculations, press the $\boxed{AC}$ button (or the $\boxed{ON/C}$ button). This will ensure that any numbers left on the calculator from the previous calculation are erased.

Example 3
$$6 + 7.31 + 18$$

$\boxed{AC}$ $\boxed{6}$ $\boxed{+}$ $\boxed{7}$ $\boxed{\cdot}$ $\boxed{3}$ $\boxed{1}$

$\boxed{+}$ $\boxed{1}$ $\boxed{8}$ $\boxed{=}$ 31·31

Example 4
$$27 - 14$$

$\boxed{AC}$ $\boxed{2}$ $\boxed{7}$ $\boxed{-}$ $\boxed{1}$ $\boxed{4}$ $\boxed{=}$ 13

Example 5
$$36 - 5.43$$

$\boxed{AC}$ $\boxed{3}$ $\boxed{6}$ $\boxed{-}$

$\boxed{5}$ $\boxed{\cdot}$ $\boxed{4}$ $\boxed{3}$ $\boxed{=}$ 30·57

Exercise 6
$$3.48 + 5.74 - 6.32$$

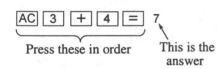

$\boxed{AC}$ $\boxed{3}$ $\boxed{\cdot}$ $\boxed{4}$ $\boxed{8}$ $\boxed{+}$

$\boxed{5}$ $\boxed{\cdot}$ $\boxed{7}$ $\boxed{4}$ $\boxed{-}$

$\boxed{6}$ $\boxed{\cdot}$ $\boxed{3}$ $\boxed{2}$ $\boxed{=}$ 2·9

Exercise 1
Use your calculator to do these

1) 4.3 + 7.5   2) 3.6 + 9.4
3) 5.15 + 3.61   4) 3.84 + 2.95
5) 6.7 - 3.4   6) 12.86 - 9.35
7) 7.82 - 6.14   8) 15.21 - 7.63
9) 9.4 + 3.7 - 6.2
10) 8.4 - 3.4 + 2.6
11) 8.7 + 2.45 - 7
12) 6.4 + 9.81 - 6.3
13) 2.41 + 8.31 - 5
14) 2.87 + 8.61 - 4.32

Multiplying and Dividing

Multiplication and Division is carried out using the $\boxed{\times}$, $\boxed{\div}$ and $\boxed{=}$ buttons

Example 7

$$3 \times 4$$

$\boxed{AC}$ $\boxed{3}$ $\boxed{\times}$ $\boxed{4}$ $\boxed{=}$ 12

Example 8

$$15 \times 36$$

$\boxed{AC}$ $\boxed{1}$ $\boxed{5}$ $\boxed{\times}$ $\boxed{3}$ $\boxed{6}$ $\boxed{=}$ 540

Example 9

$$7.8 \times 19.4$$

$\boxed{AC}$ $\boxed{7}$ $\boxed{\cdot}$ $\boxed{8}$ $\boxed{\times}$

$\boxed{1}$ $\boxed{9}$ $\boxed{\cdot}$ $\boxed{4}$ $\boxed{=}$ 151.32

Example 10

$$150 \div 30$$

$\boxed{AC}$ $\boxed{1}$ $\boxed{5}$ $\boxed{0}$ $\boxed{\div}$ $\boxed{3}$ $\boxed{0}$ $\boxed{=}$ 5

Example 11

$$28.5 \div 1.5$$

$\boxed{AC}$ $\boxed{2}$ $\boxed{8}$ $\boxed{\cdot}$ $\boxed{5}$

$\boxed{\div}$ $\boxed{1}$ $\boxed{\cdot}$ $\boxed{5}$ $\boxed{=}$ 19

Example 12

$$421.2 \div 27$$

$\boxed{AC}$ $\boxed{4}$ $\boxed{2}$ $\boxed{1}$ $\boxed{\cdot}$ $\boxed{2}$

$\boxed{\div}$ $\boxed{2}$ $\boxed{7}$ $\boxed{=}$ 15·6

Exercise 2

1) 9×15 2) 23×15
3) 37×19 4) 26.1×13
5) 32.3×27 6) 19.4×8.6
7) 12.41×3.6 8) 8.4×2.1
9) $108 \div 12$ 10) $182 \div 14$
11) $43.2 \div 12$ 12) $42.5 \div 3.4$
13) $50.44 \div 5.2$ 14) $286.44 \div 23.1$
15) $967.6 \div 23.6$ 16) $1722.63 \div 27.3$

Examples involving rounding off

Example 13

$$3.542 \times 2.614$$

$\boxed{AC}$ $\boxed{3}$ $\boxed{\cdot}$ $\boxed{5}$ $\boxed{4}$ $\boxed{2}$ $\boxed{\times}$

$\boxed{2}$ $\boxed{\cdot}$ $\boxed{6}$ $\boxed{1}$ $\boxed{4}$ $\boxed{=}$ 9.258788

or 9.259 to 3 decimal places

Example 14

$$8.964 \div 3.218$$

$\boxed{AC}$ $\boxed{8}$ $\boxed{\cdot}$ $\boxed{9}$ $\boxed{6}$ $\boxed{4}$ $\boxed{\div}$

$\boxed{3}$ $\boxed{\cdot}$ $\boxed{2}$ $\boxed{1}$ $\boxed{8}$ $\boxed{=}$ 2.7855811

or 2.786 to 3 decimal places

Exercise 3

Calculate each of the following correct to 3 decimal places.

1) 4.387×2.819 2) 3.641×4.821
3) 17.77×3.941 4) $6.78 \div 3.215$
5) $4.815 \div 2.615$ 6) $7.384 \div 2.899$
7) 7.682×3.415 8) 6.821×2.987
9) 5.431×2.675 10) $12.64 \div 3.815$
11) $37.65 \div 2.156$ 12) $14.321 \div 7.615$
13) 0.325×0.014 14) 0.821×0.00156
15) 0.14×0.015 16) $3.482 \div 7.931$
17) $6.421 \div 16.31$ 18) $0.641 \div 9.314$

Approximating Money

Example 1
Consider this problem

£71.00 is to be divided equally between 6 people. How much do they each get?

If we do this by using a pencil and paper method, this is what we get.

$$6{\overline{\smash{\big)}\,7^11\cdot0^50^20}} \quad \begin{array}{c} 1\,1\cdot8\,3\ \ r2 \end{array}$$

This calculation has been done to show 2 decimal places. These places indicate pence.

So £71.00 ÷ 6 = £11.83 with 2 pence left over.

If this is done on a calculator then the answer will be 11.833333

Clearly this cannot be written as a practical answer. However we can round off the answer to the nearest penny and say

£71.00 ÷ 6 is approximately equal to £11.83

Exercise 1
Use your calculator to give answers to each of the following, correct to the nearest penny.

1) £47 ÷ 6	2) £85 ÷ 7
3) £96 ÷ 11	4) £50 ÷ 9
5) £81 ÷ 7	6) £93 ÷ 9
7) £76.50 ÷ 7	8) £83.40 ÷ 9
9) £36.20 ÷ 11	10) £47.40 ÷ 12
11) £91.45 ÷ 13	12) £53.24 ÷ 7
13) £154.23 ÷ 14	14) £257.23 ÷ 19

Example 2
If £71 is divided equally amongst 9 people, how much do they each get?

£71 ÷ 9 = £7.8888889

In most money questions we round off to the nearest penny as a penny is the lowest monetary value we usually have to deal with.

So £71 ÷ 9 = £7.89 correct to the nearest penny.

But we would need more than £71 to give everyone £7.89. So a more practical answer would be to say they all receive £7.88 with some money left over.

This is an example of making sense of the decimal places in an answer.

In such a case we would always round down.

Example 3
£48 is divided equally between seven people. How much do they each get?

$$48 ÷ 7 = 6.8571429$$

So they each get £6.85 with some money left over.

Note. To calculate the amount left over, multiply £6.85 by 7 then subtract it from £48

i.e. £6.85 × 7 = £47.95

Amount left over is £48.00 − £47.95 = 5p

Exercise 2
Use your calculator to give answers to each of the following. In each case round the answer down.

1) £56 ÷ 9	2) £37 ÷ 7
3) £46.50 ÷ 11	4) £49.30 ÷ 6
5) £8.67 ÷ 9	6) £14.33 ÷ 13
7) £8.47 ÷ 6	8) £23.37 ÷ 14
9) £316.37 ÷ 9	10) £18.43 ÷ 13
11) £87.56 ÷ 21	12) £97.43 ÷ 15
13) £19.93 ÷ 6	14) £18.84 ÷ 37

Calculating a fraction of something

On page 26 there is a rule for calculating a fraction of something.

To find a fraction of something, divide by the denominator and multiply by the numerator.

The following examples show you how to use a calculator to do this.

Example 1

Calculate $\frac{3}{8}$ of 4.73 metres.

i.e. $4.73 \div 8 \times 3$

$\boxed{AC}\ \boxed{4}\ \boxed{\cdot}\ \boxed{7}\ \boxed{3}\ \boxed{\div}$

$\boxed{8}\ \boxed{\times}\ \boxed{3}\ \boxed{=}$ 1.77375

or 1.774 metres (to 3 decimal places)

Example 2

Calculate $\frac{2}{7}$ of 5.1 kilograms

i.e $5.1 \div 7 \times 2$

$\boxed{AC}\ \boxed{5}\ \boxed{\cdot}\ \boxed{1}\ \boxed{\div}$

$\boxed{7}\ \boxed{\times}\ \boxed{2}\ \boxed{=}$ 1.4571429kg

or 1.457 kg (to 3 decimal places)

Exercise 1

Calculate each of the following to 3 decimal places

1) $\frac{3}{7}$ of 19 metres 2) $\frac{2}{11}$ of 23 metres

3) $\frac{5}{9}$ of 25 metres 4) $\frac{5}{7}$ of 14.3kg

5) $\frac{2}{3}$ of 20kg 6) $\frac{7}{9}$ of 13kg

7) $\frac{3}{8}$ of 154 metres 8) $\frac{5}{12}$ of 16.7 metres

9) $\frac{3}{7}$ of 2.4 metres 10) $\frac{7}{15}$ of 7 litres

11) $\frac{4}{9}$ of 23.2 litres 12) $\frac{11}{15}$ of 17 litres

Calculating a percentage of something

Think of the percentage as a fraction and do the calculation in the way the previous questions were done.

Example 3

43% of 16.3 metres

this is $\frac{43}{100}$ of 16.3 metres

i.e. $16.3 \div 100 \times 43$

$\boxed{AC}\ \boxed{1}\ \boxed{6}\ \boxed{\cdot}\ \boxed{3}\ \boxed{\div}\ \boxed{1}\ \boxed{0}\ \boxed{0}$

$\boxed{\times}\ \boxed{4}\ \boxed{3}\ \boxed{=}$ 7.009 metres

Example 4

73.5% of 453 litres

i.e. $453 \div 100 \times 73.5$

$\boxed{AC}\ \boxed{4}\ \boxed{5}\ \boxed{3}\ \boxed{\div}\ \boxed{1}\ \boxed{0}\ \boxed{0}$

$\boxed{\times}\ \boxed{7}\ \boxed{3}\ \boxed{\cdot}\ \boxed{5}\ \boxed{=}$ 332.955 litres

or 333 litres (to the nearest litre)

Exercise 2

1) 17% of 33kg
2) 23% of 48kg
3) 78% of 97kg
4) 66% of 26 metres
5) 23.5% of 17 metres
6) 79.5% of 24 metres
7) 93.25% of 13.4 litres
8) 16.8% of 19.7 litres
9) 27.6% of 27.6 litres
10) 47.2% of 63.8 litres
11) 54.8% of 65.4kg
12) 97.4% of 53.2 metres

The Fraction Key

To do this you will need a scientific calculator

There are two buttons on the calculator which allow you to work directly with fractions. These are labelled

$$\boxed{\text{a}\%} \text{ and } \boxed{\%}$$

In some cases one button is used for both functions. One of the functions uses only the button, the other function uses the shift key (sometimes called the second function key) followed by the button. Refer to your calculator instruction booklet for more information about this.

The first button $\boxed{\text{a}\%}$

This allows you to put in a fraction such as $3\frac{4}{9}$ (the 'a' refers to the 3, the 'b' refers to the 4 and the 'c' refers to the 9)

Example 1
To put $3\frac{4}{9}$ into the calculator.

Press these buttons in order

$$\boxed{3} \ \boxed{\text{a}\%} \ \boxed{4} \ \boxed{\text{a}\%} \ \boxed{9}$$

This shows $3\lrcorner4\lrcorner9$ which is the calculator representation of $3\frac{4}{9}$

Example 2
$$1\frac{1}{4} + 2\frac{1}{4}$$

$$\boxed{\text{AC}} \ \boxed{1} \ \boxed{\text{a}\%} \ \boxed{1} \ \boxed{\text{a}\%} \ \boxed{4} \ \boxed{+}$$
$$\boxed{2} \ \boxed{\text{a}\%} \ \boxed{1} \ \boxed{\text{a}\%} \ \boxed{4} \ \boxed{=}$$

This gives the answer $3\lrcorner1\lrcorner2$ which is the calculator representation of $3\frac{1}{2}$

Example 3
$$3\frac{3}{13} - 1\frac{2}{5}$$

$$\boxed{\text{AC}} \ \boxed{3} \ \boxed{\text{a}\%} \ \boxed{3} \ \boxed{\text{a}\%} \ \boxed{1} \ \boxed{3}$$
$$\boxed{-} \ \boxed{1} \ \boxed{\text{a}\%} \ \boxed{2} \ \boxed{\text{a}\%} \ \boxed{5} \ \boxed{=}$$

This gives the answer $1\lrcorner54\lrcorner65$
i.e. $1\frac{54}{65}$

Exercise 1
Use the calculator to find the answer to each of the following

1) $1\frac{3}{4} + 1\frac{2}{5}$

2) $3\frac{3}{5} + 4\frac{2}{7}$

3) $5\frac{7}{9} - 2\frac{1}{2}$

4) $6\frac{7}{8} - 3\frac{3}{4}$

5) $14\frac{2}{3} + 1\frac{7}{8}$

6) $5\frac{3}{5} + 6\frac{3}{11}$

7) $4\frac{5}{13} - 3\frac{1}{2}$

8) $6\frac{7}{8} - 4\frac{9}{11}$

9) $6\frac{1}{3} + 5\frac{13}{15}$

10) $4\frac{5}{6} + 6\frac{7}{15}$

11) $3\frac{1}{2} + 2\frac{1}{5} + 1\frac{7}{8}$

12) $5\frac{2}{9} + 6\frac{4}{5} - 1\frac{4}{9}$

When using fractions by themselves, rather than mixed numbers, they are entered as follows.

$\frac{1}{2}$ is entered as $\boxed{1} \ \boxed{\text{a}\%} \ \boxed{2}$ and shows up on the calculator as $1\lrcorner2$

Example 4

$$\frac{7}{8} + \frac{5}{9}$$

Which gives $1\,31\,72$ which means $1\frac{31}{72}$

Exercise 2
Calculate each of the following

1) $\frac{3}{4} + \frac{9}{10}$ 2) $\frac{3}{4} + \frac{3}{5}$ 3) $\frac{9}{14} + \frac{3}{8}$

4) $\frac{5}{6} + \frac{7}{8}$ 5) $\frac{3}{5} - \frac{1}{4}$ 6) $\frac{9}{10} - \frac{1}{3}$

7) $\frac{4}{7} - \frac{1}{6}$ 8) $\frac{5}{9} - \frac{2}{5}$ 9) $1\frac{1}{2} + \frac{9}{13}$

10) $2\frac{1}{4} + \frac{9}{11}$ 11) $3\frac{7}{8} - \frac{5}{9}$ 12) $2\frac{1}{2} - \frac{12}{13}$

Using the function $\boxed{\%}$

This is used to change a mixed number into an improper fraction. This is why both functions have a 'c' underneath ($a\frac{b}{c}$ and $\frac{d}{c}$)

Note. The $\boxed{\%}$ button is the same button as the $\boxed{a\%}$ button but you will have to press the $\boxed{INV}$ or $\boxed{2ndF}$ or $\boxed{SHIFT}$ key first, depending on the calculator you are using.

Example 5

$3\frac{1}{2}$ as an improper fraction is $\frac{7}{2}$.

On the calculator

$$\boxed{AC}\ \boxed{3}\ \boxed{a\%}\ \boxed{1}\ \boxed{a\%}\ \boxed{2}\ \boxed{(=)}\ \boxed{\%}$$

gives $7\,2$

or $\frac{7}{2}$

Note that the "=" button is sometimes not needed, depending on the type of calculator you use.

Exercise 3
Change into improper fractions and decimal fractions, correct to 2 decimal places

1) $3\frac{7}{8}$ 2) $4\frac{3}{4}$ 3) $5\frac{3}{5}$

4) $6\frac{7}{8}$ 5) $4\frac{9}{10}$ 6) $8\frac{7}{13}$

7) $7\frac{3}{11}$ 8) $6\frac{9}{19}$ 9) $5\frac{4}{11}$

10) $6\frac{8}{17}$ 11) $10\frac{4}{21}$ 12) $6\frac{3}{19}$

Converting from fractions to decimals
This is achieved by pressing the $\boxed{a\%}$ button a second time.

Example 6

$3\frac{1}{2}$ is equal to 3.5

$$\boxed{AC}\ \boxed{3}\ \boxed{a\%}\ \boxed{1}\ \boxed{a\%}\ \boxed{2}\ \boxed{=}$$

gives $3\,1\,2$

However if you press the $\boxed{a\%}$ button again you will get 3.5

Exercise 4
Change each of the following into a decimal number by using the $\boxed{a\%}$ button.

1) $1\frac{7}{8}$ 2) $3\frac{3}{4}$ 3) $9\frac{7}{10}$

4) $6\frac{7}{8}$ 5) $9\frac{7}{40}$ 6) $12\frac{8}{25}$

7) $14\frac{7}{16}$ 8) $22\frac{7}{25}$ 9) $16\frac{7}{50}$

10) $15\frac{5}{16}$ 11) $28\frac{1}{32}$ 12) $19\frac{7}{32}$

Changing Fractions into Decimals

(See also 'Fractions, Decimals and Percentages' on page 53)

This is carried out by dividing the numerator by the denominator on the calculator

Example 1

$\frac{1}{3} = 1 \div 3 = 0.3333333$

$= 0.333$ to 3 decimal places.

Example 2

$\frac{3}{7} = 3 \div 7 = 0.4285714$

$= 0.429$ to 3 decimal places

Example 3

$\frac{9}{11} = 9 \div 11 = 0.8181818$

$= 0.818$ to 3 decimal places

Why round off?

In lots of answers on the calculator we end up with more figures than we need.

Look at the example which changes $\frac{1}{3}$ into a decimal.

On the calculator we get 0.3333333 (more or less 3's, depending on the calculator being used).

This means $\frac{3}{10} + \frac{3}{100} + \frac{3}{1000} + \frac{3}{10000}$

$+ \frac{3}{100000} + \frac{3}{1000000} + \frac{3}{10000000}$

When we compare $\frac{3}{10}$ with $\frac{3}{10000000}$ the latter number seems very small.

So the earlier figures in the number tell us the approximate value of $\frac{1}{3}$ and are necessary, whereas the later figures add very little to its value. We therefore have to make a decision as to how accurate we want our answer to be and round off accordingly.

Exercise

Change the following fractions into decimals. In each case give your answer correct to 3 decimal places.

1) $\frac{1}{9}$ 2) $\frac{7}{12}$ 3) $\frac{3}{11}$ 4) $\frac{1}{11}$

5) $\frac{1}{7}$ 6) $\frac{5}{17}$ 7) $\frac{8}{13}$ 8) $\frac{4}{9}$

9) $\frac{6}{19}$ 10) $\frac{8}{23}$ 11) $\frac{9}{14}$ 12) $\frac{5}{13}$

13) $\frac{5}{23}$ 14) $\frac{10}{21}$ 15) $\frac{7}{17}$ 16) $\frac{4}{11}$

Estimating is carried out when an accurate answer is not important. This is especially useful when a calculator is not available. Use approximations to 1 significant figure to do this.

Note that 1 significant figure means rounding off to the largest position in the number.

For example 426 becomes 400
2896 becomes 3000
16,454 becomes 20,000
etc

Multiplications

Example 1

184×320

Round up the 184 to 200
Round down the 320 to 300
so $200 \times 300 = 60,000$
i.e. 184×320 is approximately 60,000

Example 2

276×42.5

Round up the 276 to 300
Round down the 42.5 to 40
so $300 \times 40 = 12,000$
i.e. 276×42.5 is approximately 12,000

Example 3

843×72.6

Round down the 843 to 800
Round down the 72.6 to 70
So $800 \times 70 = 56,000$
i.e. 843×72.6 is approximately 56,000

Exercise 1

Calculate approximate answers to each of these multiplications

1) 87×92
2) 43×28
3) 6.3×9.8
4) 27.4×52.8
5) 542×7.6
6) 487×94
7) 22.6×981
8) 83.2×126
9) 841×6.8
10) 56.5×282
11) 3221×8.9
12) 374×243

Divisions

This is carried out by rounding off to one significant figure and then dividing. However, this does not always work as the division may not yield a simple answer. In such a case we have to do a 'fiddle'.

Example 3

$520 \div 33$

Rounding off gives $500 \div 30$
But since the point of this is to get an approximate answer, we can now 'fiddle' the numbers to make them easier to work with.

We could try increasing one number
i.e. $600 \div 30 = 20$
or the other number
i.e. $500 \div 50 = 10$
or we might 'see' that 25 divides into 500 exactly
i.e. $500 \div 25 = 20$
or increase both the numbers
i.e. $600 \div 40 = 15$
(only if you can 'see' that 40 divides into 600 exactly)

Exercise 2

Calculate approximate answers to each of these divisions.

1) $123 \div 8$
2) $96 \div 12$
3) $143 \div 13$
4) $231 \div 17$
5) $209 \div 21$
6) $321 \div 33$
7) $285 \div 26$
8) $345 \div 32$
9) $412 \div 43$
10) $743 \div 24$
11) $562 \div 14$
12) $531 \div 28$
13) $365 \div 41$
14) $876 \div 37$
15) $934 \div 63$
16) $543 \div 75$

Mental Arithmetic

There are some rules which can be of help when carrying out mental arithmetic.

Addition
Example 1
Add together 27 and 36

Say 36 + 7 = 43
43 + 20 = 63

Example 2
Add together 24 and 87

Say 87 + 4 = 91
91 + 20 = 111

Subtraction
Some subtraction can be done very quickly using 'pencil and paper' methods in your head.

Example 3
87 – 24

say 8 – 2 = 6
7 – 4 = 3
so 87 – 24 = 63

But most questions are not as easy as this. The method which works for all subtraction is the "counting on" method.

Example 2
84 – 27
Start at the lowest number and count on.

27 to 30 is 3
27 to 80 is 53
27 to 84 is 57
so 84 – 27 = 57

Exercise 1

1) 61 + 24	2) 53 + 17	3) 47 + 28
4) 56 + 26	5) 37 + 48	6) 83 + 76
7) 37 – 23	8) 84 – 51	9) 81 – 54
10) 93 – 39	11) 56 – 29	12) 83 – 47

Test yourself with others, using your calculator to check.

Mental estimation of money
Quick addition
Example 3
£5.43 + £3.91 + £8.62 + £1.43 + £3.95
+ 65p + 20p
Round these off to the nearest £
= £5 + £4 + £9 + £1 + £4 + £1 + £0 = £24

Exercise 2
Use this method to get an estimate for each of the following, then calculate the actual value to see how close it is.
1) £3.76 + £5.22 + 34p + £0.54 + £1.87
2) £1.98 + £5.76 + 38p + 67p + £3.65
3) £4.87 + £2.76 + £7.54 + 54p + £0.32
4) £5.32 + £4.87 + 76p + 45p + £0.15
5) 56p + 43p + 67p + £2.87 + £6.76 + 43p
6) £1.65 + £7.48 + 54p + £0.38 + £1.83
7) £1.76 + £8.54 + £1.59 + 54p + £1.68
8) 97p + 54p + 32p + £0.54 + £3.87 + 32p
9) £1.74 + £3.84 + £6.83 + £2.52 + 42p
10) £5.72 + 82p + 46p + £1.73 + £5.74

Adding 99p's
Example 4
£3.99 + £8.99 + £6.99 + £3.99
call this £4 + £9 + £7 + £4 – 4p
= £24 – 4p = £23.96

Exercise 3
Add together the following
1) £3.99 + £4.99 + £12.99 + 99p + £2.99
2) £0.99 + £5.99 + £6.99 + £1.99 + £2.99
+ £8.99 + £4.99
3) £8.99 + £5.99 + 99p
4) £2.99 + £6.99 + £7.99 + £7.99 + £0.99
+ 99p + 99p + £2.99 + £4.99 + £6.99
5) £2.99 + £6.99 + £8.99 + £7.99
6) £3.99 + £10.99 + £13.99 + £5.99 + 99p

Recap Test 5 - Calculator, Estimation and Mental Arithmetic

Use a calculator to do questions 1 to 13

1) a) 4.87 + 3.14 + 8.64 + 19.31
   b) 12.4 + 56.3 + 15.798 + 23.54

2) a) 27.3 − 9.45
   b) 19.05 − 15.07

3) a) 19.23 × 5
   b) 8.04 × 9

4) Calculate, giving your answer correct to 2 decimal places
   a) 5.38 ÷ 2.61   b) 19.01 ÷ 5.19

5) Calculate, giving your answer correct to the nearest penny.
   a) £4.37 ÷ 6   b) £13.98 ÷ 11

6) If £77 is divided equally amongst 6 people, how much do they each get and how much is left over?

7) a) What is $\frac{3}{5}$ of 19 metres?

b) What is $\frac{7}{20}$ of 3 litres?

8) Calculate 27% of £4.26, correct to the nearest penny.

9) What is $17\frac{1}{2}\%$ of £14.00?

10) What is $17\frac{1}{2}\%$ of £8.25, correct to the nearest penny?

11) a) Calculate $1\frac{3}{5} + 2\frac{2}{7}$, leaving your answer as a mixed number.
b) Calculate $3\frac{3}{8} + 5\frac{2}{9}$, writing your answer down in decimal form, correct to 2 decimal places.

12) Change $\frac{4}{9}$ into a decimal, correct to 3 decimal places.

13) Change $1\frac{3}{7}$ into a decimal and round it off to 3 decimal places.

In questions 14 to 16, do an estimate in your head. Write down how you do it.

14)   a) 47 × 32   b) 156 × 330

15)   a) 120 ÷ 9   b) 367 ÷ 19

16) £3.40 + £2.20 + £1.53 + £2.76 + £5.42 + 86p

In questions 17 and 18, calculate the correct answer in your head, without writing anything down other than the answer.

17) a) 24 + 32   b) 96 + 53
    c) 47 + 39   d) 88 + 74
    e) 38 − 14   f) 53 − 29
    g) 84 − 48   h) 91 − 39

18) £3.99 + £2.99 + 99p + £8.99 + £6.99

12 inches (12″ or in) make 1 foot (1′ ft)

3 ft make 1 yard (yd)

36 in make 1 yd

1760 yd make 1 mile

There are other imperial lengths which are now rarely used. Some of these are

22 yd make 1 chain

10 chains make 1 furlong

8 furlongs make 1 mile

The distance between the wickets of a cricket pitch is 1 chain. Furlongs are still quoted in horse racing.

Converting from one unit into another.

Example 1

Change 2′6″ into inches

$$2'6'' = 2 \times 12 + 6 \text{ inches}$$
$$= 24 + 6$$
$$= 30 \text{ inches}$$

Example 2

Change 50 in into feet and inches

$$50'' = 50 \div 12$$
$$= 4 \text{ r } 2$$
$$= 4 \text{ feet 2 inches}$$

Example 3

Change 3 yd 2 ft into feet

$$3 \text{ yd 2 ft} = 3 \times 3 + 2$$
$$= 9 + 2$$
$$= 11 \text{ feet}$$

Example 4

Change 1 yard 2 feet 6 inches into inches

$$1 \text{yd 2ft 6in} = (1 \times 3 + 2)\text{ft 6in}$$
$$= 5\text{ft 6in}$$
$$= 5 \times 12 + 6 \text{ inches}$$
$$= 60 + 6 \text{ inches}$$
$$= 66 \text{ inches}$$

Example 5

Change 103 inches into yards feet and inches

$$103\text{in} = 103 \div 12$$
$$= 8 \text{ r } 7$$
$$= 8\text{ft 7in}$$
$$= (8 \div 3)\text{yd 7in}$$
$$= 2\text{yd 2ft 7in}$$

Exercise 1

1) Change into feet and inches

a) 49 inches   b) 73″   c) 92in

2) Change into yards, feet and inches

a) 63in   b) 84 inches   c) 103″

3) Change into inches

a) 4 feet   b) 2yd   c) 1yd 2ft

d) 1ft 3in   e) 4′5″   f) 6yd 7in

4) Change into feet

a) 7yd   b) 10yd 2ft   c) 16yd

Adding and Subtracting

Example 6

Add together 2ft 9in, 1yd and 1ft 11in

Write down the values underneath each other, according to the dimensions.

yd	ft	in
	2	9
1	0	0
	1	11

Then, beginning with the inches column, add the numbers together, changing them into other units when necessary.

Adding the inches gives 20 in which is 1ft 8in.

yd	ft	in
	2	9
1	0	0
	1	11
		8

Adding the feet i.e. 2 + 1 + 1 = 4ft

or 1yd 1ft

yd	ft	in
	2	9
1	0	0
	1	11
2	1	8
1	1	

Finally, add the yards.

Example 7

3yd 1ft – 1yd 2ft

Do this by counting on

Starting at 1yd 2ft

from 1yd 2ft to 2yd is 1ft

from 2yd to 3yd 1ft is 1yd 1ft

So from 1yd 2ft to 3yd 1ft is 1yd 1ft + 1ft

=1yd 2ft

Example 8

2ft 3in – 1ft 9in

from 1ft 9in to 2ft is 3in

from 2ft to 2ft 3in is 3in

So from 1ft 9in to 2ft 3in is 3 + 3

= 6 inches

Example 9

2yds 1ft 3in – 1yd 2ft 7in

from 1yd 2ft 7in to 2yd is 5in

from 2yd to 2yd 1ft 3in is 1ft 3in

So from 1yd 2ft 7in to 2yd 1ft 3in is

1ft 3in + 5in = 1ft 8in.

Exercise 2

1) Add together

a) 6ft 4in + 5ft 7in + 3′4″

b) 3yd 2ft 7in + 1yd 1ft 7in + 11in

c) 2yd 2ft 2in + 4′5″ +33 inches

2) Subtract

a) 3yd – 5ft

b) 3yd 1ft – 1yd 2ft

c) 2ft 3in – 1ft 2in

d) 3ft 5in – 1ft 7in

e) 5′4″ – 2′8″

Metric and Imperial

The following are approximate relationships

1 inch = 2.54 cm

1 foot = 30.48cm (or 30.5 or $30\frac{1}{2}$ cm)

1 metre = 39.4 inches (or $39\frac{1}{2}$ in)

1 mile = 1.6km

From the above, a rough guide is to say

a) 1 inch is about $2\frac{1}{2}$ centimetres

b) A 12 inch ruler (1ft) is now a 30cm ruler

c) 1 yard is 36 inches so a metre is about 10% longer than a yard

d) A mile is a little over $1\frac{1}{2}$ km.

Examples. (All done on a calculator)

10) Change 20 inches into centimetres.

20 in = 20 × 2.54

= 50.8cm

11) Change 40cm into inches

40cm = 40 ÷ 2.54

= 15.75 inches

12) Change 14 metres into yards

14 metres = 14 × 39.4

= 551.6 inches

= 551.6 ÷ 36

= 15.32 yards.

13) Change 14 feet into metres

14 feet = 14 × 30.48 centimetres

= 426.72 cm

= 4.27 metres

(correct to 2 decimal places)

Exercise 3

Use a calculator to change these. Give your answer to 1 decimal place.

1) 9in into cm   2) 50in into cm

3) 20 metres into yd   4) 50yd into m

5) 26 ft into metres   6) 7 m into ft

7) 3 miles into km   8) 20km to miles

9) 5′9″ into cm   10) 1.4m into ft

11) $4\frac{1}{2}$ miles to km   12) 100m into yd

20 fluid ounces (fl oz) make 1 pint (pt)

8 pints make 1 gallon (gall)

There are other imperial capacities which we no longer use. One which is used in the U.S.A. is the quart, which is equal to 2 pints. (i.e. a quarter of a gallon)

Example 1

Change 2 pints 4 fluid ounces into fluid ounces

$$2\text{pt } 4\text{fl oz} = 2 \times 20 + 4$$
$$= 40 + 4$$
$$= 44\text{fl oz}$$

Example 2

Change 86 fluid ounces into pints and fluid ounces

$$86\text{fl oz} = 86 \div 20$$
$$= 4 \text{ r } 6$$
$$= 4 \text{ pints } 6 \text{ fluid ounces}$$

Example 3

Change 9 gallons 5 pints into pints

$$9 \text{ gallons } 5 \text{ pints} = 9 \times 8 + 5$$
$$= 72 + 5$$
$$= 77 \text{ pints}$$

Example 4

Change 57 pints into gallons and pints

$$57 \text{ pints} = 57 \div 8$$
$$= 7 \text{ r } 1$$
$$= 7 \text{ gallons } 1 \text{ pint}$$

Exercise 1

1) Change into pints and fluid ounces

a) 37fl oz   b) 96fl oz   c) 103fl oz

2) Change into fluid ounces

a) 5 pints   b) 3 pints 14fl oz

c) $7\frac{1}{2}$ pints   d) 5 pints 11fl oz

e) $\frac{1}{4}$ pint   f) 14 pints

3) Change into gallons and pints.

a) 20 pints   b) 82 pints   c) 96 pints

4) Change into pints

a) $6\frac{1}{2}$ gallons   b) 4 gallons 6 pints

c) $3\frac{3}{4}$ gallons

Adding and subtracting

Example 5

Add together 3 pints 15fl oz and 5 pints 9fl oz

Pints	fl oz
3	15
5	9
9	4
1	24

First $15 + 9 = 24$fl oz $= 1$ pint 4fl oz

then $3 + 5 + 1 = 9$ pints

So 3 pints 15fl oz + 5 pints 9fl oz
$= 9$ pints 4fl oz

Example 6

Add together 4 gallons 5 pints and 3 gallons 7 pints

gallons	pints
4	5
3	7
8	4
1	12

First $5 + 7 = 12$ pints $= 1$ gallon 4 pints

then $4 + 3 + 1 = 8$ gallons

So 4gall 5pt + 3galls 7pt
$= 8$gall 4pt

Example 7

3 pints 4fl oz $-$ 2 pints 9fl oz

By counting on

from 2 pints 9fl oz to 3 pints is 11fl oz

from 3 pints to 3 pints 4fl ozs is 4fl oz

So from 2 pints 9fl oz to 3 pints 4fl oz is
$$11 + 4 = 15\text{fl oz}$$

Example 8
5 gallons 3 pints − 2 gallons 6 pints
from 2gall 6 pints to 3gall is 2 pints
from 3gall to 5gall 3pts is 2gall 3pts
So from 2gall 6 pints to 5galls 3 pints is
       2 gallons 3 pints + 2 pints
          = 2 gallons 5 pints

Exercise 2
1) Add together
a) 3 pints 6fl oz + 12fl oz + 7 pints
        + 3 pints 4fl oz
b) $3\frac{1}{2}$ pints + $6\frac{1}{4}$ pints + 2 pints 11fl oz
c) 3 gallons + 2 gallons 4 pints + 7 pints
d) 9 gall 6 pints + $2\frac{1}{2}$ gall + $5\frac{3}{4}$ gall
2) Subtract
a) 5 pints − 15fl oz
b) $4\frac{1}{2}$ pints − 1 pint 3fl oz
c) 8 pints 6fl oz − $\frac{3}{4}$ pint
d) 2 gallons − 3 pints
e) 9 gallons 6 pints − $4\frac{1}{2}$ gallons

Relationship between common metric and imperial measurements
The following are approximate relationships

---

       1 litre = 1.76 pints
       1 gallon = 4.55 litres

From the above, a rough guide is
      1 litre is about $1\frac{3}{4}$ pints
      1 gallon is about $4\frac{1}{2}$ litres

Examples (all done on a calculator)
9) Change 20 litres into pints.
     20 litres = 20 × 1.76 pints
            = 35.2 pints

10) Change 45 litres into gallons
     45 litres = 45 ÷ 4.55
           = 9.9 gallons
    (correct to 1 decimal place)

11) Change 5 gallons into litres
     5 gallons = 5 × 4.55
           = 22.75 litres

12) Change 26 pints into litres
     26 pints = 26 ÷ 1.76
          = 14.8 pints
   (correct to 1 decimal point)

Exercise 3
Use a calculator to change each of the following correct to 1 decimal place.
 1) 14 gallons into litres
 2) 23 gallons into litres
 3) 12 pints into litres
 4) 35 pints into litres
 5) 14 litres into pints
 6) 43 litres into pints
 7) 17 litres into gallons
 8) 36 litres into gallons
 9) What is more, 10 gallons or 40 litres?
10) The petrol tank of a car will hold 10 gallons. If it is half full, how many litres of petrol are needed to fill it up?

16 ounces (oz) make 1 pound (lb)
14 pounds make 1 stone

There are other imperial weights which are no longer used. Some of these are

8 stones make 1 hundredweight (cwt)

20 hundredweights make 1 ton.

The ton has now largely been replaced by the metric tonne (both pronounced in the same way) which is approximately the same weight.

(1 ton = 2240lb,

1 tonne = 1000kg = 2205lb

i.e. 1 tonne is about 98.4% of 1 ton)

Example 1

Change 3lb 5oz into ounces

$$3lb\ 5oz = 3 \times 16 + 5$$
$$= 48 + 5$$
$$= 53oz$$

Example 2

Change 37 ounces into pounds and ounces.

$$37oz = 37 \div 16$$
$$= 2\ r\ 5$$
$$= 2lb\ 5oz$$

Example 3

Change 10 stone 4 pounds into pounds.

$$10\ stone\ 4lb = 10 \times 14 + 4$$
$$= 140 + 4$$
$$= 144lb$$

Example 4

Change 108lb into stones and pounds.

$$108\ pounds = 108 \div 14$$
$$= 7\ r\ 10$$
$$= 7\ stone\ 10lb$$

Exercise 1

1) Change into pounds and ounces

a) 38oz   b) 68oz   c) 97oz

2) Change into ounces

a) 2 pounds   b) $3\frac{1}{2}$ lb   c) 2lbs 5oz

d) $1\frac{1}{4}$ lb   e) 4lbs 6oz   f) 9lbs 7oz

3) Change into stones and pounds

a) 27lb   b) 73lb   c) 140lb

4) Change into pounds

a) 9 stones   b) 4 stone 7lbs

c) 13 stone 8 pounds   d) $4\frac{1}{2}$ stone

Adding and subtracting

Example 5

Add together 3lb 10oz and 2lb 12oz

First add together the ounces.

$$10oz + 12oz = 22oz\ or\ 1lb\ 6oz$$

lb	oz
3	10
2	12
6	6
1	22

So 3lb 10oz + 2lb 12oz = 6lb 6oz

Example 6

4 stone 3 pounds + 8 stone 12 pounds

First 3lb + 12lb = 15lb or 1 stone 1lb

st	lb
4	3
8	12
13	1
1	15

So 4 stone 3lb + 8 stone 12lb
= 13 stone 1lb

Example 7

5lb 7oz – 3lb 12oz

By counting on

from 3lb 12oz to 4lb is 4oz

from 4lb to 5lb 7oz is 1lb 7oz

So from 3lb 12oz to 5lb 7oz

is 4oz + 1lb 7oz

= 1lb 11oz

Example 8
9 stone 6 pounds – 4 stone 9 pounds
from 4 stone 9lb to 5 stone is 5lb
from 5 stone to 9 stone 6lb
is 4 stone 6lb
So from 4 stone 9lb to 9 stone 6lb is
5lb + 4 stone 6lb
= 4 stone 11lb

Exercise 2
1) Add
a) 4lb 6oz + 3lbs 2oz + 5lb 14oz
b) 15oz + 9oz + 2lb + 3lb 4oz
c) 9 stone + 3 stone 4lb + 12lb + 6 stone 4lb
d) 14 stone + $9\frac{1}{2}$ stone + 4 stone 2lb
2) Subtract
a) 4lb – 12oz
b) 9lb 3oz – 5lbs 1oz
c) 10lb 4oz – 6lbs 9oz
d) 6 stone – 10lb
e) 7 stone 3lb – 4 stone 6lb

Relationships between common metric and imperial measurements
The following are approximate relationships.

---
1 ounce = 28 grams
1 pound = 454 grams
1 kilogram = 2.2 pounds

From the above, a very rough guide is to say;
1kg is about 2lb
1oz is about 30 grams.

Examples (all done on a calculator)
9) Change 500 grams into ounces
500 grams = 500 ÷ 28
= 17.9 ounces
(to 1 decimal place)

10) Change 12 ounces into grams
12 ounces = 12 × 28
= 336 grams
11) Change 1lb 4oz into grams
1lb 4oz = 454g + 4 × 28g
= 454 + 112 grams
= 566 grams
12) Change 4kg into pounds
4kg = 4 × 2.2
= 8.8lb
13) Change 27lb into kg
27lb = 27 ÷ 2.2
= 12.3kg (to 1 d.p.)
14) Change 5 stone 4 pounds into kg.
5stone 4lb = 5 × 14 + 4
= 70 + 4
= 74lb
74 pounds = 74 ÷ 2.2
= 33.6kg (to 1 d.p)

Exercise 3
Use a calculator to change each of the following correct to 1 decimal place.
1) 106 grams into ounces
2) 2 ounces into grams
3) 11 pounds into kilograms
4) 4lb into grams
5) 1lb 9oz into grams
6) $7\frac{1}{2}$ lb into kg.
7) 19lb into kg.
8) 7 kilograms into pounds
9) $12\frac{1}{2}$ kg into lb.
10) $17\frac{1}{2}$ oz into grams
11) 200 grams into ounces
12) 10 stone into kg.
13) 13 stone 12lb into kg.
14) 105kg into stones and pounds.

Roman Numerals

Roman numerals are still used today but in a very limited way. Compared with todays decimal system it would be very difficult to do calculations with them. They are used to show years, usually at the end of films, on old buildings etc. They are also sometimes used as page numbers. For example a film made in 1963 might have MCMLXIII on its credits, and a building from 1880 might have MDCCCLXXX. Page lxvi can be used instead of page 66. The Romans used the following letters.

I represented 1
V represented 5
X represented 10
L represented 50
C represented 100
D represented 500
M represented 1000

To obtain other numbers between these, the letters were added together.
For example

III means 3 (1+1+1)
VI means 6 (5 + 1)
XI means 11 (10 + 1)
XV means 15 (10 + 5)
LX means 60 (50 +10)
LXI means 61 (50 + 10 + 1)
MDC means 1600 (1000 + 500 + 100)
and so on

Exercise 1
Say what each of the following represent.

i) XXI	ii) VII
iii) XVI	iv) XXXVI
v) LXV	vi) CXVII
vii) CXXVII	viii) CLXVIII
ix) CCCLXVI	x) DXXVII
xi) DCXV	xii) DCCLXV
xiii) MXXX	xiv) MDCXV

This method relies entirely on adding numbers together and can get quite complicated. In order to ease this the Romans began to write down numbers as subtractions.

Example
MDCCCC represents 1900
(1000 + 500 + 400)
but this can be done more economically by saying 1000 + 900
i.e. MCM   (CM means 100 before 1000)
Other numbers that can be simplified in this way

4 becomes IV and not IIII (1 before 5)
9 becomes IX and not VIIII (1 before 10)
14 becomes XIV and not XIIII
(10 and 1 before 5)
and so on

Exercise 2
Say what numbers each of the following represent.

i) XC	ii) CXC	iii) XD
iv) XM	v) MXM	vi) MCMIII
vii) MCML	viii) XLV	ix) CM
x) CDV	xi) CMIX	xii) XMV

Exercise 3
The following dates have appeared on buildings or at the end of film credits, indicating the year they were built or produced. In each case write down the year and put them in order, oldest first.

i) MDCCLIV	ii) MDCCCLXXXIV
iii) MCM	iv) MCMLXIX
v) MCMXLIII	vi) MCMLXXXIV
vii) MDCXLIII	viii) MDCCCLXIII
ix) MDCCI	x) MDCCXXXVII
xi) MCMXCV	xii) MDCLXXXVII
xiii) MDCCCVI	xiv) MCMXXVII

Probability

Probability is a measure of the chance of something happening. Some things are easy to measure and some are difficult. For example, if a coin is tossed the outcome can be either heads or tails. Both outcomes are equally likely to happen. It is equally likely to come down heads as it is to be tails. The chance of it being heads is 50-50, or 50% or $\frac{1}{2}$. However, to calculate the probability that it will rain in two weeks time is a lot more difficult to do as many factors need to be taken into account.

Example 1
A bag contains 3 discs, each exactly the same to the touch. One is red, one is blue and one is green. What is the probability or chance of putting your hand in the bag and taking out the green one?

The chance of getting the green disc is 1 chance in 3, since there is one green disc and three discs altogether.

Probability (green) = 1 in 3 or $\frac{1}{3}$

Example 2
A dice is rolled. What is the probability that the number 2 is on the top?
This time the chance is 1 in 6 i.e. we want to get one of the six numbers.
$$\text{Prob (2)} = \frac{1}{6}$$

Rule
Probability of something happening
$$= \frac{\text{Number of outcomes we want}}{\text{Total number of outcomes}}$$

Example 3
10 cards have the numbers 1 to 10 written on them.

| 1 | 2 | 3 | 4 | 5 | 6 | 7 | 8 | 9 | 10 |

The cards are shuffled and placed face down on a table. A card is chosen. Calculate the probability of each of the following happening.
a) The card chosen will have the number 6 on it.
b) The number on the card will be greater than 6.
c) the number on the card will not be 6.

a) Here one card from the pack of ten cards needs to be chosen.
$$\text{Prob (6)} = \frac{1}{10} \text{ or 0.1 or 10\%}$$
b) Here a 7, 8, 9 or 10 is needed. i.e. any one of these four cards will do.
$$\text{Prob (6 or more)} = \frac{4}{10} = \frac{2}{5} \text{ or 0.4 or 40\%}$$
c) Here 1, 2, 3, 4, 5, 7, 8, 9, or 10 is needed. i.e anything except for 6
$$\text{Prob (not 6)} = \frac{9}{10} \text{ or 0.9 or 90\%}$$

Exercise 1
Calculate the probability of the events in questions 1 to 5 happening.

1) Throwing the number 5 on a dice numbered 1 to 6.

2) Drawing a queen (4 queens to a pack) from a pack of 52 playing cards.

3) Selecting a female name at random from a list containing 20 females and 15 males.

4) Winning first prize in a raffle if you have 5 tickets and 90 tickets have been sold altogether.

5) Throwing an even number on a dice numbered 1 to 6.

6) The order of play in a tennis competition is decided by drawing names from a hat. Six names, Sarah, Joanne, Claire, Tracey, Dianne and Susan are put into a hat and drawn out one at a time. What is the probability
a) of getting Joannes name first?
b) of not getting Joannes name first?
c) of getting Sarah, Joanne or Claire first?

7) A bag contains 18 discs, 6 red, 8 green and 4 yellow. A disc is taken out at random. What is the probability of drawing
a) a green disc?
b) a red disc?
c) a yellow disc?

8) In a raffle, 500 tickets are sold. Winston buys 15 tickets.
a) What is his chance of winning?
b) If the chance of David winning is 5%, how many tickets does he buy?

The probability of something happening is given a number. As has been shown above, this number lies between 0 and 1.

For example, the chance of getting the number 4 on a dice is $\frac{1}{6}$. The chance of getting 1, 2, 3, 5 or 6 on the dice is $\frac{5}{6}$.

If the number does not appear on the dice, say the number 7, then the chance of getting it is 0.

If we ask what is the chance of getting 1, 2, 3, 4, 5, or 6 on the dice, then this chance is 6 chances out of 6 or $\frac{6}{6}$ or 1.

So 0 represents no chance of something happening and 1 represents certainty.

There are situations where these two extremes occur.

The probability of the sun rising tomorrow is 1.

The probability that a person will live to the age of 500 is 0.

If the probability of something happening is close to 1 then it has a very good chance of happening.

If the probability of something happening is close to 0, then it has a poor chance of happening.

This can be shown on a number line.

No chance — Even chance — Certainty

0 — Poor chance — 0.5 — Good chance — 1

Exercise 2

List the following in order of their chance of happening, according to what you know of the situation.

a) When a stone is thrown upwards, it will fall to earth.

b) It will rain tomorrow.

c) The next person to telephone you will be male.

d) The birthday of the next person to telephone you will be in November.

e) A new television set will break down within a week of buying it.

f) A television set will break down at least once in the first eight years of its life.

1) Change 57 inches into feet and inches.

2) Change 10′6″ into yards, feet and inches.

3) Change 2 yards 2 feet into inches.

4) Add together 6ft 4ins and 1yd 2ft.

5) Subtract 13 inches from 2′7″.

6) If 1 inch is equal to 2.54 centimetres, change;
a) 26 inches into centimetres.
b) 30 centimetres into inches.

7) Change 53 fluid ounces into pints and fluid ounces.

8) Change 25 pints into gallons and pints.

9) Add together 4 pints and 27 fluid ounces, giving your answer as pints and fluid ounces.

10) Subtract $3\frac{1}{2}$ gallons from 50 pints.

11) If 1 gallon is approximately equal to $4\frac{1}{2}$ litres, change;
a) 6 gallons into litres.
b) 36 litres into gallons.

12) Change 57 ounces into pounds and ounces.

13) Change $3\frac{1}{2}$ stones into pounds.

14) Subtract $5\frac{1}{2}$ stones from 7 stones 12 pounds.

15) If 1 kilogram is approximately equal to 2.2lbs, change;
a) 7kg into lbs.
b) 30lbs into kg.

16) What numbers do the following Roman numerals represent?
a) XVII   b) XL   c) CLX   d) MCXI

17) Write down the following numbers as Roman numerals;
a) 79   b) 156   c) 453   d) 1941

18) A bag contains 10 snooker balls, all similar to the touch. 7 are red, 1 is black, 1 is blue and 1 is pink. If 1 ball is withdrawn from the bag, what is the probability that it is
a) red   b) not red   c) blue?

Use a calculator only where you are told to.

1) Round off these numbers to the nearest 10 a) 49 b) 83 c) 145 d) 863 e) 1456

2) Add together 37, 43, 89 and 241.

3) A case of wine contains 12 bottles. In a store room there are 47 cases.
a) What would you write down to estimate the number of bottles in the store?
b) Write down a sum and calculate the exact number of bottles.

4) Subtract 98 from 153.

5) Add together one thousand three hundred and eighty six with nine hundred and sixty two.

6) What is $542 - 367$?

7) What is the value of the 6 in the number 3652?

8) What is 302×27?

9) Change $\frac{3}{8}$ into a decimal number, without using a calculator.

10) Calculate $2457 \div 33$. What is the remainder?

11) Compare these three fractions and put them down in order of size, smallest first.

$\qquad$ 25%, $\qquad \frac{1}{5}$, $\qquad$ 0.23

12) Write down the answer to 700×600.

13) Calculate 40% of £1.50.

14) What is 3562 to the nearest 100?

15) William gets a mark of 45 out of 50 in his mathematics test. What is this as a percentage?

16) A bag contains 8 yellow sweets, 6 red sweets and 3 green sweets. What fraction of the sweets are
  a) yellow,   b) red,   c) green?

17) Value added tax of $17\frac{1}{2}$ % is added on to the cost of work done by a plumber. What is the total cost for a job costing £40?

18) Calculate $\frac{9}{10}$ of 30.

19) Write down, without doing any calculations, the answers to these;
a) 16×10 b) 127×1000 c) 8.7×100

20) What is $\frac{10}{15}$ in its lowest terms?

21) What must 238 be multiplied by to get 2,380,000?

22) Change $\frac{15}{10}$ into a mixed number in its lowest terms.

23) Calculate $285 \div 7$, showing your remainder.

24) What is $1\frac{3}{4} + 3\frac{1}{2}$?

25) Calculate the exact answer to $25.4 \div 4$

26) Calculate $3\frac{7}{8} - 2\frac{1}{4}$

27) Calculate 453×16

28) Calculate $\frac{5}{6} \times \frac{3}{4}$

29) Use a calculator to do these. Give your answer correct to 1 decimal place.
a) 0.384×27 b) 1.31×2.8 c) 9.71×27.6

30) What is $\frac{3}{4} \div \frac{1}{2}$?

31) On a market stall, apples are sold at 8 for £1.28. On another stall the same apples are sold at 12 for £1.80. Which stall is selling them cheapest?

32) Calculate $2\frac{1}{4} \div \frac{3}{8}$

33) Divide £630 between two people so that one gets twice as much as the other.

34) Split up 30 into the ratio 2:3.

35) Liam makes some chocolate buns. The recipe below will make 8 buns.
  50g of butter
  150ml of water
  60g of flour
  6 eggs

170g chocolate

a) Liam wants to make 12 buns. How much of each ingredient will he need?

b) Last week Liam's wife made 30 buns. How much of each ingredient did she use?

36) Write down $\frac{14}{100}$ as a decimal.

37) A car was bought for £4000 and sold at a 30% profit. How much was it sold for?

38) Calculate 24.3 – 17.4

39) This table shows the evening programmes on television.

    6:00pm Six O'Clock News
    6:30 Regional News
    7:00 Holiday Show
    7:30 Cartoon
    7:40 The Music Programme
    8:10 Film
    9:50 Local News
    10:00 Main Evening News
    10:30 Antiques Show
    11:00 Nature Programme
    11:25 Late Show

a) How long does The Music Programme last?

b) How long does the Film last?

c) Claire has a 3 hour video tape. She records the Film and the Antiques Show. Will she have enough space left on the tape to record the Nature Programme?

40) Calculate 3.1 × 0.21

41) In each of the following patterns, write down the next two numbers;
  a) 6, 11, 16, 21, 26...
  b) 27, 27, 26, 24, 21...

42) What is 37.4 ÷ 5?

43) The distance from Sarah's home to the centre of London is 56 miles. What is the approximate distance in kilometres?

44) Round off 3.586 to 2 decimal places.

45) Calculate the area of this shape.

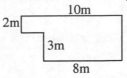

46) If £3.43 is divided equally between 3 people, how much do they each get and how much is left over?

47) Joe leaves home at 07:05 and takes 32 minutes to get to work. His friend, Bill, leaves home at 06:51 and takes 39 minutes to get there. Who arrives at work first?

48) What is 17% of £500?

49) Say whether the following are likely, unlikely, or have an even chance of happening.
a) Throwing a 1 on a dice
b) Throwing a 6 on a dice
c) Throwing an odd number on a dice
d) Drawing a green disc from a bag of 100 discs containing 70 green discs.

50) Change 55% into a fraction in its lowest terms.

51) What is the probability of getting the number 2 when throwing a dice?

52) What is 37% as a decimal?

53) Calculate the average (mean) of the numbers
  13, 5, 10, 11, 12, 13, 14, 15, 10, 12

54) What is 16.4821 rounded off to the nearest whole number?

55) Estimate 1573 ÷ 42. Show the numbers you would use.

56) What is 27.81583 rounded off to 3 decimal places?

57) What is three hundred and forty subtract ninety two?

58) The temperature of peas in a freezer is –18°C. They are heated up in a pan to 88°C. What is the increase in temperature?

59) Change these into percentages.

a) $\frac{3}{20}$ b) $\frac{25}{40}$ c) $\frac{24}{50}$

60) In a shop a skirt has been reduced in price from £39 to £19. Use your calculator to work out the percentage reduction. Give your answer correct to 1 decimal place.

61) Rhys earns £450 a week. He pays £180 in tax. What fraction of his wages does he pay in tax and what is this as a percentage?

62) Change 4.3kg into grams.

63) In a sale, the price of a shirt was reduced by $\frac{1}{3}$. If its original price was £18.60, what is its new price?

64) A wine bottle contains 75cl when full. Two glasses, each of 17.5cl, are poured. How much wine is left in the bottle?

65) Use your calculator to work out 63% of £51.40 correct to the nearest penny.

66) Calculate the final temperature if
  a) –2°C increases by 4°C
  b) –6°C falls by 5°C

67) A box is in the shape of a cuboid. It's volume is 500 cubic centimetres. If it's base measures 12.5cm by 5cm, what is it's height?

68) At midnight the temperature was –10°C. At midday it had risen to 2°C. What was the change in temperature?

69) Jane buys four items of clothing in a shop. They cost £7.99, £3.99, £6.99 and £4.99. What mental calculation could she do to calculate the final cost?

70) What must 0.087 be divided by to get 0.00087?

71) Use the fraction button on your calculator to do these;

a) $\frac{1}{4} + \frac{5}{6}$ b) $2\frac{1}{7} - 1\frac{1}{2}$ c) $3\frac{7}{8} - \frac{9}{10}$

72) Subtract XXV from LXXXIV, giving your answer as Roman numerals.

73) Use your calculator to change these fractions into decimals

a) $\frac{5}{8}$ b) $\frac{1}{20}$ c) $3\frac{1}{4}$

74) A TV costs £105 deposit and 20 weekly payments of £5.37. What is the total cost?

75) David buys 21p stamps and 28p stamps from the post office with a £5 note. If he buys 14 stamps at 21p, how many stamps at 28p can he buy?

76) What is 457 in Roman numerals?

77) Divide £700 into the ratio 7:3

78) An amount of money was shared between two people in the ratio 5:4. If the first person got £200, how much did the other get?

79) A man weighs 12 stone 5lbs and his wife weighs 8 stone 12lbs. What is their combined weight?

80) In a country of 9,000,000 inhabitants 2 in every 7 own a car. Use your calculator to find how many own a car, correct to the nearest 100

81) Ian Jones buys his goods at £200 each and sells them at £260 each. What is his percentage profit?

82) Write down the next three numbers in the pattern;
    128, 64, 32, 16...

83) Add together 6′4″ and 1′9″.

84) A bottle contains $2\frac{1}{2}$ litres of milk. If $\frac{1}{4}$ of it is taken out, how much remains?

85) A ferry leaves port at 22:43 on Tuesday. It arrives at its destination at 06:05 on Wednesday. How long does the journey take?

86) Victoria's height is 5′4″ and her husband's height is 6′1″. What is the difference in their heights?

87) Use your calculator to change $\frac{2}{7}$ into a

decimal correct to 3 decimal places.

88) Two towns are 20 miles apart. A train leaves the first town at 10:15 a.m. It travels to the other town at an average speed of 60 m.p.h. At what time will it arrive?

89) The probability of some events happening are given by the numbers
0, 0.1, 0.3, 0.5, 0.7, 0.9 and 1.0
The same events have the following chances of happening;
likely, even, very unlikely, no chance, very likely, unlikely and certain. Match the number to each of the chances.

90) Barchester United Football club score an average (mean) of 2.5 goals in six games.
a) What was their total score?
b) In their next game they score 5 goals. Is this sufficient to bring the average up to 3?

91) What is the change in temperature between −7°C and −19°C?

92) Calculate $\frac{5}{12}$ of £75.

93) How many $\frac{1}{1000}$ths are there in $\frac{1}{10}$th?

94) The distance between two towns is $43\frac{1}{3}$ kilometres. Sarah's car will do $8\frac{1}{2}$ kilometres to each litre of petrol. Use the fraction button on the calculator to find how many litres of petrol the car will use on the journey.

95) What is the area of a rectangle measuring 5.4 metres by 500cms?

96) A cardboard box is in the shape of a cuboid measuring 6cm by 12cm by 15cm. Calculate its volume.

97) An open tank is in the shape of a cuboid. Its base measures 50cm by 80cm and its height is 40cm. Calculate;
a) its volume in cubic centimetres.
b) its capacity in litres.

98) A car travels at an average speed of 60k.p.h. How far will it travel in;

a) $\frac{1}{2}$ hour   b) 2 hours   c) $\frac{1}{4}$ hour?

99) The LCM of 4 and 6 is 12. What is the LCM of 4, 6 and 10?

100) Jim's lawn measures $12\frac{1}{4}$ metres by $9\frac{3}{4}$ metres. He spreads weed killer on the lawn. The instructions say that each 10 grams of weed killer will cover $5\frac{1}{2}$ square metres.
Use a calculator to find;
a) the area of the lawn
b) the amount of weed killer he will need, correct to the nearest 10 grams.

101) Calculate the average speed of a car which travels 94 miles in 3 hours, then 58 miles in 2 hours and finally 93 miles in 2 hours.

102) A bag contains 15 discs, 5 red, 6 green and 4 blue. A disc is taken out at random. What is the probability of getting;
a) a green disc
b) a red disc
c) a disc which is not blue?

103) A car travels a distance of 340 miles and uses 8 gallons of petrol. What is it's average fuel consumption?

104) A kitchen floor measures 3 metres by 2.6 metres. It is to be covered by tiles measuring 20cm square.
a) How many tiles will be needed along the 3m edge?
b) How many tiles will be needed along the 2.6m edge?
c) How many tiles will be needed altogether?
Tiles can only be bought in packs of 10. How many packs will be needed?

Answers

Saying and writing numbers   Page 7
Exercise 1
1) 76 2) 327 3) 400 4) 850 5) 906 6) 1,436 7) 6,000 8) 11,400 9) 27,060 10) 70,004
11) 163,956 12) 607,089 13) 1,500,000 14) 63,409,628 15) 109,000,063 16) 342,806,327
17) 7,000,000,000 18) 8,506,000,000 19) 100,000,000,000
Exercise 2
1) seventy nine 2) six hundred and forty one 3) one thousand, three hundred and fourteen 4) nine thousand, three hundred and two 5) eighteen thousand and four 6) twenty six thousand three hundred and fifteen 7) one hundred and eighty four thousand three hundred and twenty six 8) nine hundred and forty thousand five hundred and twenty one 9) six hundred thousand 10) one million four hundred thousand 11) eight million four hundred and twenty one thousand 12) twenty seven million three hundred and fourteen
Exercise 3
1) 160 2) 3,200 3) 100,000 4) 640,000 5) 346,000 6) 10,000,000 7) 999,999 8) 140,865
Place value   Page 9
1) six tens 2) six units 3) six tens 4) six hundred 5) six thousand 6) six hundred 7) sixty thousand 8) sixty thousand 9) six hundred 10) six hundred 11) sixty thousand 12) six thousand 13) six hundred thousand 14) six hundred thousand 15) six hundred 16) sixty million 17) sixty thousand 18) six million 19) six million 20) six million
Addition   Page 10
Exercise 1
1) 25 2) 168 3) 388 4) 397 5) 576 6) 869 7) 679 8) 795 9) 999 10) 889 11) 868 12) 888
Exercise 2
1) 629 2) 1024 3) 819 4) 828 5) 909 6) 827 7) 650 8) 931 9) 929 10) 862 11) 916 12) 870
13) 926 14) 949
Exercise 3
1) 143 2) 940 3) 1600 4) 5263 5) 5299 6) 11,803 7) 607 8) 1192 9) 2304 10) 9779 11) 6071
12) 11,955
Subtraction   Page 12
Exercises 1 and 5
1) 7 2) 11 3) 22 4) 28 5) 47 6) 75 7) 11 8) 17 9) 46 10) 106 11) 114 12) 221 13) 114
14) 228 15) 159 16) 228 17) 329 18) 213 19) 1336 20) 2606
Exercises 2 and 6
1) 293 2) 362 3) 491 4) 161 5) 474 6) 291 7) 251 8) 282
Exercise 3 and 7
1) 176 2) 465 3) 288 4) 158 5) 177 6) 88 7) 137 8) 175
Exercises 4 and 8
1) 297 2) 788 3) 575 4) 868 5) 457 6) 548 7) 410 8) 111 9) 227 10) 826 11) 658 12) 4574
Number patterns   Page 16
Exercise 1
1) 42, 49, 56 2) 54, 63, 72 3) 25, 29, 33 4) 15, 17, 19 5) 22, 25, 28 6) 28, 33, 38 7) 48, 57, 66
Exercise 2
1) 18, 24, 31 2) 15, 20, 26 3) 35, 47, 61 4) 17, 23, 30 5) 35, 41, 48 6) 23, 30, 38 7) 39, 51, 65
Exercise 3
1) 15, 13, 11 2) 16, 12, 8 3) 35, 31, 27 4) 27, 24, 21 5) 15, 8, 0 6) 37, 25, 11 7) 40, 30, 19

Multiplication　Page 17

Exercise 1

1) 84　2) 86　3) 99　4) 85　5) 182　6) 148　7) 258　8) 420　9) 384　10) 712

Exercise 2

1) 308　2) 1376　3) 901　4) 1392　5) 1696　6) 2688　7) 546　8) 4524　9) 3276　10) 6080

Exercise 3

1) 1802　2) 4851　3) 9504　4) 12,958　5) 21,896　6) 19,320　7) 18,116　8) 38,352　9) 54,936
10) 85,347

Short division　Page 18

1) 44　2) 71　3) 89 r2　4) 48 r6　5) 97 r1　6) 107 r5　7) 397　8) 39 r 5　9) 90 r2　10) 173 r3
11) 93 r3　12) 231 r3　13) 73 r3　14) 127 r3

Long division　Page 19

1) 12　2) 12 r5　3) 14　4) 15　5) 22 r12　6) 37　7) 34 r5　8) 52 r2　9) 29 r3　10) 51　11) 15 r7
12) 107　13) 21 r39　14) 36　15) 31 r5　16) 63　17) 23 r15　18) 37　19) 23 r11　20) 32 r8
21) 47 r37　22) 64　23) 41 r47　24) 153

Rounding off and estimating　Page 20

Exercise 1

1) 70　2) 90　3) 140　4) 250　5) 180　6) 170　7) 350　8) 550　9) 680　10) 760　11) 880　12) 950

Exercise 2

1) 30　2) 5000　3) 600　4) 3000　5) 300　6) 170　7) 480　8) 140　9) 7000　10) 900　11) 5000
12) 1400　13) 6000　14) 100　15) 3400　16) 1300　17) 9000　18) 5000　19) 190　20) 18,000
21) 350　22) 36,000　23) 6000　24) 4000　25) 400　26) 250　27) 8400　28) 11,200　29) 11,200
30) 11,000　31) a) 23,000　b) 23,300　c) 23,250

Multiplying numbers ending with zeros　Page 21

Exercise 1

1) 80　2) 900　3) 2000　4) 61,000　5) 270　6) 34,000　7) 86,000　8) 90,000　9) 43,140　10) 78,400
11) 9,530　12) 864,000

Exercise 2

1) 300　2) 400　3) 350　4) 3200　5) 1800　6) 6000　7) 100,000　8) 42,000　9) 120,000　10) 90,000
11) 1,400,000　12) 4,200,000　13) 12,000,000　14) 35,000,000　15) 48,000,000　16) 140,000,000

Recap test 1　Page 22

1) a) 167　b) 16,400　c) 156,343　d) 6,000,006　2) a) sixty eight　b) one hundred and fifty seven
c) seven thousand four hundred and eighty two　d) twelve thousand four hundred and twenty one
e) two hundred and fifty six thousand, four hundred and twenty one　f) three million
g) five million, four hundred thousand　h) sixteen million, two hundred and fifty four thousand
3) a) 250　b) 100,000　c) 5000　d) 852,500　4) a) hundreds　b) units　c) tens　d) thousands　e) millions
f) hundred thousands　5) 27, 500, 572, 684, 1432, 9142, 81, 562, 934, 381, 8million　6) a) 99
b) 258　c) 2210　d) 4010　e) 3932　7) a) 23　b) 14　c) 245　d) 144　e) 841　8) a) 18　b) 24　c) 35
d) 48　e) 56　f) 54　g) 63　h) 81　i) 72　9) a) 36, 42, 48　b) 30, 28, 26　c) 25, 32, 40　d) 46, 33, 18
10) a) 54　b) 1551　c) 11,664　11) a) 145 r2　b) 106 r1　c) 37 r9　d) 75 r21　12) a) 70　b) 90　c) 700
d) 1500　e) 12,400　f) 650　13) a) 120　b) 1500　c) 8000　d) 30,000　e) 420,000　f) 15,000,000
g) 1,200,000　h) 150,000,000

Definition of a fraction　Page 23

1) a) $\frac{5}{8}$　b) $\frac{3}{8}$　2) a) $\frac{7}{15}$　b) $\frac{8}{15}$　3) a) $\frac{5}{12}$　b) $\frac{7}{12}$　4) a) $\frac{17}{25}$　b) $\frac{8}{25}$　5) a) $\frac{4}{7}$　b) $\frac{3}{7}$　6) a) $\frac{5}{11}$　b) $\frac{2}{11}$
c) $\frac{1}{11}$　d) $\frac{1}{11}$　e) $\frac{2}{11}$　7) a) $\frac{9}{17}$　b) $\frac{5}{17}$　c) $\frac{3}{17}$

Calculating a part of something　Page 25

Exercise 1

1) no　2) yes　3) $\frac{1}{8}$　4) 2　5) 2　6) 4　7) $\frac{1}{12}$　$\frac{1}{8}$　$\frac{1}{7}$　$\frac{1}{5}$　$\frac{1}{4}$　$\frac{1}{3}$　$\frac{1}{2}$

Exercise 2
1) 10 2) 5 3) 3 4) 7 5) 5 6) 6 7) 5 8) 10 9) 3 10) 5 11) 4 12) 8 13) 8 14) 10cm
15) 6 hours 16) 6 17) 2 18) 6 19) 10mm 20) 5

Exercise 3
1) $\frac{4}{5}$ 2) $\frac{7}{10}$ 3) $\frac{5}{7}$ 4) $\frac{5}{8}$ 5) $\frac{3}{5}$ 6) $\frac{5}{6}$ 7) $\frac{5}{9}$ 8) $\frac{11}{16}$ 9) $\frac{9}{20}$ 10) $\frac{7}{12}$ 11) $\frac{11}{18}$ 12) $\frac{11}{20}$

Exercise 4
1) 8 2) 15 3) 9 4) 9 5) 15 6) 15 7) 20 8) 21 9) 20 10) 12 11) 45 12) 15 13) 30 14) 21
15) 14 16) 25 17) 48 18) 56

Equivalent fractions   Page 27
1) $\frac{1}{4}$ 2) $\frac{1}{5}$ 3) $\frac{1}{4}$ 4) $\frac{1}{5}$ 5) $\frac{1}{3}$ 6) $\frac{1}{3}$ 7) $\frac{2}{5}$ 8) $\frac{3}{4}$ 9) $\frac{3}{4}$ 10) $\frac{2}{5}$ 11) $\frac{3}{7}$ 12) $\frac{2}{3}$ 13) $\frac{2}{3}$ 14) $\frac{2}{3}$ 15) $\frac{3}{5}$
16) $\frac{6}{9}$ $\frac{8}{12}$ $\frac{10}{15}$ $\frac{12}{18}$ $\frac{4}{6}$ $\frac{18}{27}$ $\frac{14}{21}$ 17) $\frac{5}{25}$ $\frac{12}{30}$ $\frac{12}{20}$ $\frac{12}{15}$

Mixed numbers   Page 28
Exercise 1
1) $2\frac{2}{5}$ 2) $3\frac{1}{2}$ 3) $3\frac{1}{3}$ 4) $2\frac{3}{4}$ 5) $3\frac{3}{4}$ 6) $5\frac{2}{3}$ 7) $4\frac{1}{5}$ 8) $3\frac{3}{8}$ 9) $3\frac{4}{9}$ 10) $4\frac{7}{10}$ 11) $5\frac{6}{7}$ 12) $2\frac{7}{13}$

Exercise 2
1) $\frac{3}{2}$ 2) $\frac{9}{4}$ 3) $\frac{15}{4}$ 4) $\frac{8}{3}$ 5) $\frac{11}{5}$ 6) $\frac{22}{7}$ 7) $\frac{11}{4}$ 8) $\frac{7}{2}$ 9) $\frac{13}{5}$ 10) $\frac{19}{8}$ 11) $\frac{26}{7}$ 12) $\frac{33}{10}$

Adding fractions   Page 29
2) $\frac{5}{6}$ 3) $\frac{5}{6}$ 4) $\frac{7}{24}$ 5) $\frac{13}{30}$ 6) $\frac{8}{15}$ 7) $\frac{1}{2}$ 8) $\frac{9}{10}$ 9) $\frac{11}{12}$ 10) $\frac{7}{10}$ 11) $\frac{2}{5}$ 12) $\frac{19}{24}$ 13) $\frac{7}{15}$ 14) $\frac{23}{24}$
15) $\frac{31}{36}$ 16) $\frac{17}{20}$ 17) $\frac{2}{3}$ 18) $\frac{1}{2}$ 19) $\frac{39}{40}$ 20) $\frac{19}{24}$ 21) $\frac{15}{16}$

Mixed number answers   Page 30
Exercise 1
1) $1\frac{3}{8}$ 2) $1\frac{3}{10}$ 3) $1\frac{17}{36}$ 4) $1\frac{11}{18}$ 5) $1\frac{2}{3}$ 6) $1\frac{7}{40}$ 7) $1\frac{23}{40}$ 8) $1\frac{17}{40}$ 9) $1\frac{1}{3}$ 10) $1\frac{11}{36}$

Exercise 2
1) $3\frac{3}{4}$ 2) $4\frac{1}{2}$ 3) $3\frac{5}{8}$ 4) $8\frac{7}{8}$ 5) $4\frac{1}{10}$ 6) $11\frac{9}{20}$ 7) $11\frac{11}{12}$ 8) $7\frac{1}{2}$ 9) $5\frac{7}{10}$ 10) $6\frac{3}{8}$ 11) $12\frac{3}{8}$ 12) $7\frac{13}{16}$
13) $9\frac{3}{10}$ 14) $6\frac{1}{8}$

Exercise 3
1) $\frac{3}{8}$ 2) $\frac{3}{10}$ 3) $\frac{1}{9}$ 4) $1\frac{1}{12}$ 5) $2\frac{1}{8}$ 6) $1\frac{7}{15}$ 7) $2\frac{7}{20}$ 8) $3\frac{11}{16}$ 9) $2\frac{1}{5}$ 10) $2\frac{1}{5}$ 11) $3\frac{23}{60}$ 12) $2\frac{7}{12}$

Exercise 4
1) $3\frac{3}{8}$ 2) $1\frac{13}{16}$ 3) $2\frac{13}{20}$ 4) $1\frac{3}{8}$ 5) $2\frac{1}{2}$ 6) $1\frac{10}{21}$ 7) $\frac{19}{20}$ 8) $2\frac{11}{24}$ 9) $2\frac{5}{12}$ 10) $3\frac{17}{21}$

Exercise 5
1) $4\frac{19}{20}$ 2) $1\frac{4}{15}$ 3) $1\frac{2}{3}$ 4) $1\frac{13}{20}$ 5) $2\frac{19}{24}$ 6) $2\frac{1}{15}$ 7) $\frac{11}{16}$ 8) $2\frac{3}{10}$ 9) $\frac{5}{9}$ 10) $3\frac{1}{6}$ 11) $2\frac{16}{21}$ 12) $2\frac{11}{20}$
13) $2\frac{13}{21}$ 14) $3\frac{1}{16}$ 15) $4\frac{1}{2}$ 16) $6\frac{27}{40}$

Multiplication of fractions   Page 32
Exercise 1
1) $4\frac{1}{2}$ 2) $1\frac{1}{2}$ 3) $5\frac{1}{4}$ 4) $2\frac{1}{2}$ 5) $2\frac{3}{4}$ 6) 15 7) $10\frac{1}{2}$ 8) $32\frac{1}{4}$ 9) $24\frac{3}{8}$ 10) $31\frac{1}{2}$ 11) $29\frac{2}{5}$ 12) $24\frac{3}{4}$
13) $37\frac{5}{8}$ 14) $32\frac{1}{5}$ 15) 32

Exercise 2

1) $\frac{9}{16}$ 2) $\frac{5}{16}$ 3) $\frac{8}{27}$ 4) $\frac{3}{25}$ 5) $\frac{5}{32}$ 6) $\frac{21}{40}$ 7) $\frac{8}{15}$ 8) $\frac{4}{7}$ 9) $\frac{7}{25}$ 10) $\frac{21}{44}$ 11) $\frac{5}{12}$ 12) $\frac{11}{24}$ 13) $\frac{9}{20}$
14) $\frac{2}{7}$ 15) $\frac{1}{3}$ 16) $\frac{6}{35}$ 17) $\frac{5}{42}$ 18) $\frac{35}{96}$

Exercise 3

1) $\frac{7}{10}$ 2) $1\frac{2}{5}$ 3) $1\frac{9}{16}$ 4) $\frac{39}{80}$ 5) $2\frac{11}{12}$ 6) $\frac{9}{20}$ 7) $1\frac{7}{25}$ 8) $1\frac{7}{15}$ 9) $2\frac{1}{10}$ 10) $1\frac{7}{20}$ 11) 1 12) $3\frac{1}{16}$

Exercise 4

1) $3\frac{3}{4}$ 2) 4 3) $3\frac{1}{16}$ 4) $7\frac{7}{8}$ 5) $3\frac{7}{16}$ 6) $2\frac{11}{20}$ 7) $2\frac{3}{4}$ 8) $3\frac{3}{8}$ 9) $4\frac{3}{8}$ 10) $2\frac{7}{8}$ 11) $14\frac{5}{8}$ 12) $6\frac{93}{100}$

Exercise 5

1) 6 2) 7 3) $3\frac{3}{4}$ 4) $5\frac{1}{2}$ 5) 5 6) 10 7) $6\frac{3}{4}$ 8) 14 9) $8\frac{4}{5}$ 10) $9\frac{3}{5}$ 11) $13\frac{3}{4}$ 12) $20\frac{2}{5}$

Exercise 6

1) 150 2) 65 3) $34\frac{1}{2}$ 4) $32\frac{1}{10}$ 5) $92\frac{1}{2}$ 6) 380 7) $46\frac{1}{2}$ 8) $52\frac{1}{2}$ 9) $73\frac{3}{5}$ 10) $55\frac{5}{6}$

Dividing by a fraction   Page 34
1) 12 2) 21 3) 6 4) 5 5) 18 6) $6\frac{1}{4}$ 7) $\frac{13}{16}$ 8) $3\frac{1}{3}$ 9) $\frac{5}{6}$ 10) $1\frac{11}{15}$ 11) $1\frac{3}{5}$ 12) $1\frac{1}{5}$ 13) $2\frac{5}{8}$ 14) $\frac{7}{8}$
15) $25\frac{1}{2}$ 16) $8\frac{1}{2}$ 17) $1\frac{1}{6}$ 18) $1\frac{11}{16}$ 19) $1\frac{11}{17}$ 20) $1\frac{1}{27}$ 21) $\frac{1}{2}$ 22) $\frac{13}{18}$

Ratio   Page 35
Exercise 1
1) 2:1 2) 1:4 3) 3:1 4) 5:2 5) 5:2 6) 3:7 7) 4:3 8) 4:9 9) 2:5 10) 6:1 11) 10:3 12) 6:25
13) 11:15 14) 9:19 15) 3:7
Exercise 2
1) 20:10 2) 27:18 3) 8:12 4) 24:6 5) 10:40 6) 40:20 7) 10:50 8) 30:50 9) 70:10 10) 30:40
11) 49:21 12) 30:70 13) 50:200 14) 250:100
Recap test 2   Page 37
1) a) $\frac{7}{8}$ b) $\frac{1}{6}$ c) $\frac{5}{12}$ 2) $\frac{12}{25}$ 3) $\frac{1}{12}$ $\frac{1}{9}$ $\frac{1}{7}$ $\frac{1}{6}$ $\frac{1}{5}$ $\frac{1}{4}$ $\frac{1}{3}$ $\frac{1}{2}$ 4) a) 10 b) 7 c) 6 d) 6 e) 18 f) 30 g) 24
h) 49 i) 36 5) a) $\frac{6}{7}$ b) $\frac{7}{11}$ c) $\frac{10}{13}$ 6) a) $\frac{1}{3}$ b) $\frac{1}{3}$ c) $\frac{1}{3}$ d) $\frac{3}{4}$ 7) a) $1\frac{3}{4}$ b) $1\frac{4}{5}$ c) $2\frac{1}{6}$ d) $6\frac{1}{4}$
8) a) $\frac{3}{2}$ b) $\frac{15}{4}$ c) $\frac{21}{4}$ d) $\frac{33}{5}$ 9) a) 8 b) 24 c) 18 10) a) $\frac{4}{21}$ b) $\frac{9}{10}$ c) $\frac{1}{4}$ 11) a) $1\frac{1}{4}$ b) $1\frac{5}{8}$ c) $1\frac{7}{40}$
d) $3\frac{3}{4}$ e) $10\frac{5}{8}$ f) $6\frac{1}{2}$ 12) a) $\frac{1}{4}$ b) $\frac{7}{10}$ c) $\frac{1}{8}$ d) $1\frac{3}{4}$ e) $3\frac{1}{8}$ f) $3\frac{3}{8}$ g) $2\frac{9}{10}$ h) $5\frac{19}{40}$ i) $2\frac{5}{8}$
13) a) $3\frac{1}{2}$ b) $7\frac{1}{2}$ c) $43\frac{1}{3}$ d) $1\frac{1}{8}$ e) $1\frac{2}{5}$ f) $3\frac{3}{4}$ g) $18\frac{18}{35}$ h) $14\frac{27}{32}$ i) $36\frac{3}{4}$ j) 35 k) 325 l) 6750
14) a) 26 b) $1\frac{5}{8}$ c) $\frac{1}{4}$ 15) a) 2:1 b) 3:1 c) 3:2 d) 1:4 16) a) £18:£12 b) £11.34:£4.86

Decimal fractions   Page 38
Exercise 1
1) 0.9 2) 0.09 3) 0.19 4) 0.39 5) 0.77 6) 3.3 7) 6.7 8) 24.09 9) 28.16 10) 37.53 11) 15.61
12) 76.28
Exercise 2
1) 0.007 2) 0.014 3) 0.232 4) 5.006 5) 18.009 6) 32.027 7) 56.348 8) 126.127 9) 643.08
10) 54.640
Adding and subtracting decimals   Page 39
Exercise 1
1) 4.02 2) 23.51 3) 22.125 4) 18.464 5) 135.931 6) 146.74 7) 19.455 8) 24.504 9) 155.926
10) 89.102 11) 214.36 12) 188.724 13) 184.91 14) 136.245

Exercise 2

1) 3.1 2) 3.4 3) 21.8 4) 22.04 5) 135.7 6) 11.4 7) 15.71 8) 22.89 9) 39.088 10) 13.6
11) 30.585 12) 10.828 13) 21.11 14) 33.19

Multiplying decimals   Page 41

Exercise 1

1) 16.8 2) 48.6 3) 30.65 4) 25.872 5) 17.0 6) 37.8 7) 17.24 8) 167.4 9) 299.2 10) 19.35
11) 107.1 12) 71.7

Exercise 2

1) 22.26 2) 24.5 3) 35.26 4) 6.447 5) 6.147 6) 8.46 7) 77.12 8) 41.976 9) 372.12 10) 0.390
11) 0.504 12) 5.595 13) 23.604 14) 442.32 15) 0.2835 16) 0.1264 17) 0.36630 18) 0.3212

Exercise 3

1) 0.021 2) 0.123 3) 0.7749 4) 0.0448 5) 0.2976 6) 0.02124 7) 0.5002 8) 0.6129 9) 0.000585
10) 0.0000651 11) 0.0476 12) 0.0258 13) 0.084 14) 0.02604

Multiplying and dividing by 10, 100 etc   Page 43

Exercise 1

1) 30 2) 4 3) 0.8 4) 31 5) 7.7 6) 0.65 7) 31.7 8) 6.74 9) 0.754 10) 0.06 11) 0.013 12) 0.0407
13) 0.16 14) 0.173 15) 7.15 16) 10.64 17) 3.821 18) 2.74 19) 0.0003 20) 0.08135 21) 0.00104

Exercise 2

1) 30 2) 5 3) 0.7 4) 0.08 5) 31 6) 4.7 7) 0.57 8) 0.082 9) 41.2 10) 6.53 11) 0.605 12) 0.0731
13) 31.42 14) 0.006 15) 0.00014 16) 0.00156 17) 0.0314 18) 0.1603 19) 0.00095 20) 0.01003
21) 0.00002

Exercise 3

1) 0.0268 2) 0.641 3) 0.0962 4) 0.1252 5) 0.67 6) 0.094 7) 0.00863 8) 0.204 9) 0.031
10) 0.009 11) 0.0008 12) 0.061 13) 0.0083 14) 0.00043 15) 0.006 16) 0.0008 17) 0.00609
18) 0.0264 19) 0.176 20) 0.0194

Exercise 4

1) 3 2) 1.4 3) 13.1 4) 16.0 5) 40 6) 8 7) 130 8) 2900 9) 8160 10) 274.1 11) 10670 12) 0.81
13) 60.03 14) 1001 15) 18,760 16) 43.1 17) 601.4 18) 870 19) 8710 20) 8014

Dividing decimals   Page 46

Exercise 1

1) 5.4 2) 7.75 3) 5.25 4) 5.4 5) 8.2 6) 6.3 7) 8.4 8) 6.75 9) 0.024 10) 1.6 11) 0.21 12) 22.1
13) 3.25 14) 5.23 15) 4.55 16) 0.0125 17) 0.8004 18) 2.015 19) 14.03 20) 12.5

Exercise 2

1) 0.2 2) 0.5 3) 0.3 4) 0.7 5) 0.375 6) 0.6 7) 0.625 8) 0.25 9) 0.875 10) 0.04 11) 0.15
12) 0.075 13) 0.35 14) 0.025 15) 0.3125

Rounding off decimals   Page 48

Exercise 1

1) 1.33 2) 8.94 3) 0.62 4) 9.38 5) 19.51 6) 2.81 7) 0.03 8) 0.50 9) 6.94 10) 0.79 11) 4.18
12) 14.49 13) 14.56 14) 2.82 15) 0.08 16) 8.68 17) 6.37 18) 3.20

Exercise 2

1) 0.78 2) 0.64 3) 0.27 4) 0.43 5) 0.36 6) 0.18 7) 0.14 8) 0.11 9) 0.86 10) 0.57 11) 0.22
12) 0.09 13) 0.44 14) 0.71 15) 0.89

Percentages   Page 50

Exercise 1

1) £3.40 2) 95p 3) £2.00 4) £7.50 5) £12.15 6) 60p 7) 96p 8) 21p 9) 10p 10) 75p 11) £3.50
12) £4.20

Exercise 2

1) 56 2) 55 3) 68 4) 208 5) 423 6) 140 7) 403 8) 162 9) £13.28 10) £7.36 11) £5.16
12) 56p 13) £12.18 14) £3.42 15) £1.98 16) £3.77

Changing information into a percentage   Page 52
1) 20%   2) 40%   3) 30%   4) a) 57%   b) 90%   c) 70%   d) 60%   e) 70%   f) 30%   g) 60%   h) 60%
5) 45%

Fractions, decimals and percentages   Page 53
1) 0.4   2) 31%   3) $\frac{7}{10}$ 4) $\frac{9}{10}$ 5) $\frac{19}{20}$ 6) 87.5%   7) $\frac{1}{4}$.   8) 85%   9) 72.5%   10) 30%   11) 0.75
12) $\frac{31}{50}$ 13) 45%   14) $\frac{9}{20}$ 15) $\frac{83}{100}$ 16) 80%   17) $\frac{7}{20}$ 18) 70%   19) $\frac{41}{50}$ 20) 87.5%

Rounding off decimal numbers   Page 54
Exercise 1
1) 6   2) 8   3) 9   4) 11   5) 3   6) 19   7) 22   8) 16   9) 13   10) 38   11) 4   12) 20
Exercise 2
1) 8   2) 9   3) 13   4) 9   5) 14   6) 23   7) 38   8) 52   9) 60   10) 88   11) 5   12) 6   13) 9   14) 12   15) 20
Exercise 3
1) 5   2) 10   3) 28   4) 6   5) 137   6) 16   7) 13   8) 10   9) 83   10) 132   11) 12   12) 36   13) 19
14) 17   15) 48

Rounding off to 1 decimal place   Page 55
Exercise 1
1) 7.8   2) 6.5   3) 6.3   4) 19.5   5) 29.5   6) 3.8   7) 14.9   8) 16.3   9) 5.5   10) 3.7   11) 27.7   12) 5.7
Exercise 2
1) 7.0   2) 13.0   3) 4.0   4) 6.0   5) 7.0   6) 9.0   7) 5.0   8) 20.0   9) 11.0   10) 10.0   11) 9.0   12) 5.0

Rounding off to any number of places   Page 56
1) 7.3   2) 0.07   3) 8.32   4) 7.0015   5) 0.0074   6) 10.6   7) 12.84   8) 17.42   9) 9.315   10) 16.9
11) 10.00   12) 6.814   13) 0.0090   14) 0.009   15) 3.49   16) 3.0

Recap test 3   Page 57
1) a) 0.7   b) 0.17   c) 0.053   d) 3.3   e) 17.03   18.009   2) a) 6.71   b) 20.82   c) 104.131   d) 224.1
e) 65.713   f) 15.15   g) 3.556   h) 27.64   3) a) 32.40   b) 110.40   c) 29.636   d) 0.2674   e) 0.738
f) 0.0522   4) a) 36   b) 560   c) 0.23   d) 18   e) 2654   f) 15.3   g) 20   5) a) 0.6   b) 2.7   c) 4.32   d) 0.08
e) 0.0001   f) 0.526   g) 0.0184   h) 0.0002   i) 2.703   6) a) 4.5   b) 3.7   c) 12.3   d) 0.0013   e) 1.253
7) a) 0.75   b) 0.375   c) 0.175   8) a) 3.14   b) 8.69   c) 5.98   d) 12.21   e) 7.00   f) 0.32   9) a) £15
b) £10   c) £1.20   d) 90p   e) 50p   f) £2.50   g) 60p   h) £8.75   i) £1.28   j) £6.65   10) 45%   11) 56%
12) a) 0.6   b) $\frac{8}{25}$ c) 37.5%   d) $\frac{17}{25}$ e) 75%   13) a) 27   b) 8   c) 19   14) a) 8.9   b) 17.84   c) 0.018
d) 10.0385

Thermometer Scale   Page 58
Exercise 1
1) 11°C   2) 8°C   3) 2°C   4) 3°C   5) 0°C   6) 10°C   7) –4°C   8) –3°C   9) 3°C   10) –5°C   11) 9
12) 4   13) –4   14) 2   15) 8   16) –3   17) 7   18) 6   19) 0   20) –1
Exercise 2
1) 9°C   2) 0°C   3) –2°C   4) –8°C   5) –18°C   6) –5°C   7) 4°C   8) –14°C   9) –25°C   10) –8°C
11) –4   12) –13   13) –1   14) –15   15) –13   16) –10   17) –2   18) –19   19) –19   20) –15
Exercise 3 mixed
1) 14°C   2) –12°C   3) –4°C   4) 10°C   5) 7°C   6) –6°C   7) 3°C   8) 58°C   9) a) 48°C   b) 10°C
c) 18°C   d) 6°C   e) 11°C   f) –5°C   g) –8°C   h) –7°C   i) 17°C   j) 6°C

Weight   Page 60
Exercise 1
1) 0.006kg   2) 0.012kg   3) 0.029kg   4) 0.05kg   5) 0.3kg   6) 0.304kg   7) 0.34kg   8) 0.344kg
9) 0.556kg   10) 0.671kg   11) 1.126kg   12) 2.3kg   13) 3.45kg   14) 5.6kg   15) 10kg   16) 7.141kg
17) 5.322kg   18) 8.643kg

Exercise 2
1) 30g 2) 6g 3) 310g 4) 375g 5) 14g 6) 187g 7) 400g 8) 860g 9) 34g 10) 1371g 11) 1300g
12) 1670g 13) 3700g 14) 16,400g 15) 7310g 16) 10,400g 17) 8760g 18) 9815g
Exercise 3

1) $\frac{27}{1000}$ 2) $\frac{53}{1000}$ 3) $\frac{187}{1000}$ 4) $\frac{361}{1000}$ 5) $\frac{1}{2}$ 6) $\frac{1}{4}$ 7) $\frac{1}{10}$ 8) $\frac{37}{100}$ 9) $\frac{17}{20}$ 10) $1\frac{1}{2}$ 11) $2\frac{1}{4}$ 12) $3\frac{2}{5}$
13) $1\frac{13}{20}$ 14) $2\frac{27}{1000}$ 15) $3\frac{51}{100}$ 16) $5\frac{2}{5}$ 17) $8\frac{7}{20}$ 18) $9\frac{31}{100}$

Exercise 4
1) 750g 2) 800g 3) 400g 4) 100g 5) 1500g 6) 2250g 7) 3300g 8) 3750g 9) 3050g 10) 4200g
11) 900g 12) 1170g 13) 6125g 14) 350g 15) 60g 16) 7150g 17) 9600g 18) 7125g

Capacity   Page 62
Exercise 1
1) 0.8 L 2) 0.027L 3) 0.132L 4) 0.07L 5) 0.006L 6) 0.45L 7) 6.142L 8) 4.1L 9) 0.062L
10) 0.127L 11) 0.841L 12) 1.25L 13) 1.006L 14) 12.2L 15) 3.105L 16) 4.06L 17) 15.004L
18) 4.81L
Exercise 2
1) 700ml 2) 450ml 3) 760ml 4) 934ml 5) 631ml 6) 701ml 7) 1600ml 8) 3740ml 9) 8900ml
10) 5610ml 11) 7320ml 12) 4817ml 13) 6931ml 14) 4702ml 15) 6005ml 16) 2ml 17) 9ml
18) 93ml 19) 40ml 20) 50ml 21) 5ml
Exercise 3

1) $\frac{7}{1000}$ L 2) $\frac{37}{1000}$ L 3) $\frac{149}{1000}$ L 4) $1\frac{397}{1000}$ 5) $\frac{1}{125}$ L 6) $\frac{9}{200}$ L 7) $\frac{1}{4}$ L 8) $2\frac{1}{2}$ L 9) $\frac{1}{20}$ L 10) $\frac{3}{40}$ L
11) $\frac{2}{5}$ L 12) $\frac{41}{50}$ L 13) $\frac{47}{50}$ L 14) $1\frac{1}{20}$ L 15) $2\frac{1}{20}$ L

Exercise 4
1) 500ml 2) 700ml 3) 200ml 4) 600ml 5) 2750ml 6) 3500ml 7) 25ml 8) 150ml 9) 1050ml
10) 1160ml 11) 3400ml 12) 2040ml 13) 3360ml 14) 625ml 15) 3125ml 16) 5120
Exercise 5
1) a) 0.2L b) 0.73L c) 1.2L d) 2.1L e) 3.5L f) 12L 2) a) 30cl b) 75cl c) 130cl d) 540cl
e) 1030cl f) 671cl 3) a) $\frac{1}{25}$ L b) $\frac{53}{100}$ L c) $\frac{3}{20}$ L d) $1\frac{1}{2}$ L e) $2\frac{1}{5}$ L f) 5L 4) a) 50cl b) 25cl c) 30cl
d) 35cl e) 125cl f) 312.5cl

Length   Page 64
Exercise 1

1) a) 0.09 b) $\frac{9}{100}$ m 2) a) 0.13 b) $\frac{13}{100}$ m 3) a) 0.47 b) $\frac{47}{100}$ m 4) a) 0.02 b) $\frac{1}{50}$ m 5) a) 0.26 b) $\frac{13}{50}$ m
6) a) 0.82 b) $\frac{41}{50}$ m 7) a) 0.04 b) $\frac{1}{25}$ m 8) a) 0.25 b) $\frac{1}{4}$ m 9)a) 0.96 b) $\frac{24}{25}$ 10) a) 0.15 b) $\frac{3}{20}$ m
11) a) 0.55 b) $\frac{11}{20}$ m 12) a) 0.85 b) $\frac{17}{20}$ m 13) a) 1.4 b) $1\frac{2}{5}$ m 14) a) 2.6 b) $2\frac{3}{5}$ m 15) a) 5.8 b) $5\frac{4}{5}$ m
16) a) 3.5 b) $3\frac{1}{2}$ m 17) a) 4.25 b) $4\frac{1}{4}$ m 18) a) 5.44 b) $5\frac{11}{25}$

Exercise 2
1) 8cm 2) 45cm 3) 80cm 4) 176cm 5) 194cm 6) 237cm 7) 596cm 8) 1468cm 9) 1404cm
10) 350cm 11) 425cm 12) 330cm 13) 640cm 14) 415cm 15) 568cm 16) 832cm 17) 1080cm
18) 975cm
Exercise 3
1) a) 7mm b) 20mm c) 34mm d) 80mm e) 120mm f) 234mm g) 5mm h) 2.5mm i) 15mm

2) a) 3cm b) 4.5cm c) 0.9cm d) 8.4cm e) 10.5cm f) 45cm 3) a) 1500mm b) 500mm c) 300mm
d) 90mm e) 430mm f) 320mm g) 2500mm h) 250mm i) 100mm 4) a) 2m b) 3.5m c) 0.75m
d) 0.3m e) 0.09m f) 0.064m

Exercise 4

1) a) 500m b) 250m c) 3100m d) 2500m e) 70m f) 1350m 2) a) 1.5km b) 0.2km c) 3.25km
d) 0.19km e) 1.45km f) 0.079km

Money   Page 65

Exercise 1

1) £0.09 2) £0.20 3) £0.35 4) £0.50 5) £0.84 6) £1.27 7) £2.94 8) £8.03 9) £10.01 10) £16.00
11) £27.14 12) £61.41 13) £37.40 14) £81.62 15) £194.21

Exercise 2

1) 184p 2) 245p 3) 830p 4) 604p 5) 324p 6) 23p 7) 50p 8) 308p 9) 1020p 10) 197p
11) 231p 12) 3p 13) 543p 14) 45p 15) 1037p

Exercise 3

1) £15.01 2) £16.14 3) £1.39 4) £2.11 5) £6.43 6) £ 9.37 7) £10.97 8) £19.46 9) £46.04
10) £22.21 11) £2.90 12) £13.81

Exercise 4

1) £1.13 2) £2.12 3) 16p 4) 35p 5) 45p 6) £1.24 7) 46p 8) £1.78 9) 67p 10) £2.81 11) £2.76
12) £2.34 13) £11.68 14) £3.64

Area of a rectangle   Page 66

Exercise 1

1) 15 sq m 2) 18 sq m 3) 14.1 sq cm 4) 7.41 sq cm 5) $2\frac{1}{4}$ sq m 6) $7\frac{7}{8}$ sq m 7) 72 sq cm
8) 49.8 sq cm 9) 18.8 sq cm 10) 3.84 sq cm 11) 18.06 sq cm 12) 11.18 sq cm 13) $10\frac{1}{2}$ sq cm
14) $2\frac{1}{8}$ sq cm

Exercise 2

1) 32 sq cm 2) 27 sq cm 3) 11 sq cm 4) 56 sq cm 5) 53 sq cm 6) 42 sq cm 7) 40 sq m
8) 38 sq m 9) 75 sq m 10) 18.8 sq cm 11) 43.1 sq cm 12) 36.4 sq m 13) $2\frac{1}{8}$ sq m 14) $18\frac{3}{8}$ sq m

Volume of a cuboid   Page 69

Exercise

1) 60cc 2) 20cc 3) 48cc 4) 66cc 5) 54.4cc 6) 7.2cc 7) 132cc 8) 648cc 9) 126.42cc 10) 68.88cc

Volume and capacity   Page 71

Exercise

1) 144ml 2) 108ml 3) 340ml 4) 7.128L 5) 27L 6) 1.536L 7) 17.5L 8) 43.24L 9) 2.628L
10) 163.8ml

Time   Page 72

Exercise 1

1) 07:00 2) 07:20 3) 03:45 4) 21:25 5) 00:10 6) 12:10 7) 15:45 8) 06:30 9) 14:35 10) 10:40
11) 06:30 12) 23:45 13) 00:15 14) 13:55

Exercise 2

1) a) 5hrs 30mins b) 1hr 30mins c) 1hr 45mins d) 55mins e) 1hr 45mins f) 4hrs 50mins g) 30mins
h) 2hrs 30mins i) 4hrs 45mins j) 3hrs 1min 2) 29mins 3) 35mins 4) 2hrs 30mins 5) 3hrs 55mins
6) 1hr 50mins 7) 4hrs 35mins

Exercise 3

1) 15:15 2) 1:25pm 3) 04:55 4) 04.45 5) 7:55pm 6) 9:43pm 7) 12:25pm 8) 12:17 9) 03:13
10) 04:15

Information Tables   Page 74

Question 1

a) 08:37 b) 09:52 c) 22mins d) 17:08

Question 2
a) £1319   b) £2018   c) £4156
Question 3
a) 381   b) 281   c) Glasgow and Edinburgh or Cardiff and Swansea   d) London and Glasgow
Mean (Average)   Page 75
Exercise 1
1) 6   2) 13   3) 23   4) 29.5   5) 20   6) 40   7) £9.45
Exercise 2
1) 60mph   2) 8mph   3) 2.5mph   4) 38mph   5) a) 2800km   b) 400kph   c) 16mph
Exercise 3
1) 37.5mpg   2) $7\frac{2}{3}$ km per litre   3) $8\frac{1}{2}$ km per litre   4) 31.25mpg

Recap Test 4   Page 77
1) a) 1   b) –3   c) –3   d) –6   e) –3   f) –2   2) 14°C   3) a) 2.5kg   b) 1.25kg   c) 0.645kg   d) 0.027kg
4) a) 1500g   b) 580g   c) 14g   d) 3g   e) 500g   f) 600g   g) 1050g   h) 2750g   5) a) $\frac{1}{4}$ kg   b) $\frac{3}{5}$ kg
c) $1\frac{2}{5}$ kg   d) $2\frac{9}{20}$ 6) a) 0.4L   b) 0.85L   c) 0.06L   d) 1.8L   e) 0.8L   f) 1.5L   g) 3L   h) 0.75L
7) a) 3000ml   b) 1470ml   c) 30ml   8) a) 250cl   b) 136cl   c) 8cl   9) a) 3m 40cm   b) 8m 35cm
10) a) 300mm   b) 1400mm   c) 80mm   d) 500mm   e) 5mm   f) 7.5mm   11) a) 137p   b) 42p   c) 1543p
12) a) £2.40   b) £0.16   c) £25.68   13) £6.58   14) £5.53   15) a) 7.2sq m   b) 14sq.m   c) 29sq cm
16) a) 60cc   b) 42cc   17) One cubic centimetre will hold one millilitre   18) a) 14cl or 140ml   b) 1050cl
or 10.5L   19) a) 03:30   b) 15:30   c) 00:00 or 24:00   20) a) 12:15am   b) 12:15pm   c) 5:24pm
21) 1 hour 15 minutes   22) 8:55   23) 11:52   24) 132   25) £2038   26) 25   27) 55mph
28) 7.5 miles per litre
The Calculator   Page 79
Exercise 1
1) 11.8   2) 13   3) 8.76   4) 6.79   5) 3.3   6) 3.51   7) 1.68   8) 7.58   9) 6.9   10) 7.6   11) 4.15   12) 9.91
13) 5.72   14) 7.16
Exercise 2
1) 135   2) 345   3) 703   4) 339.3   5) 872.1   6) 166.84   7) 44.676   8) 17.64   9) 9   10) 13   11) 3.6
12) 12.5   13) 9.7   14) 12.4   15) 41   16) 63.1
Exercise 3
1) 12.367   2) 17.553   3) 70.032   4) 2.109   5) 1.841   6) 2.547   7) 26.234   8) 20.374   9) 14.528
10) 3.313   11) 17.463   12) 1.881   13) 0.005   14) 0.001   15) 0.002   16) 0.439   17) 0.394   18) 0.069
Approximating money   Page 81
Exercise 1
1) £7.83   2) £12.14   3) £8.73   4) £5.56   5) £11.57   6) £10.33   7) £10.93   8) £9.27   9) £3.29
10) £3.95   11) £7.03   12) £7.61   13) £11.02   14) £13.54
Exercise 2
1) £6.22   2) £5.28   3) £4.22   4) £8.21   5) £0.96   6) £1.10   7) £1.41   8) £1.66   9) £35.15   10) £1.41
11) £4.16   12) £6.49   13) £3.32   14) £0.50
Calculating a part of something   Page 82
Exercise 1
1) 8.143m   2) 4.182m   3) 13.889m   4) 10.214kg   5) 13.333kg   6) 10.111kg   7) 57.75m   8) 6.958m
9) 1.029m   10) 3.267L   11) 10.311L   12) 12.467L
Exercise 2
1) 5.61kg   2) 11.04kg   3) 75.66kg   4) 17.16m   5) 3.995m   6) 19.08m   7) 12.4955L   8) 3.3096L
9) 7.6176L   10) 30.1136L   11) 35.8392kg   12) 51.8168m

111

The Fraction key   Page 83

Exercise 1

1) $3\frac{3}{20}$ 2) $7\frac{31}{35}$ 3) $3\frac{5}{18}$ 4) $3\frac{1}{8}$ 5) $16\frac{13}{24}$ 6) $11\frac{48}{55}$ 7) $\frac{23}{26}$ 8) $2\frac{5}{88}$ 9) $12\frac{1}{5}$ 10) $11\frac{3}{10}$ 11) $7\frac{23}{40}$
12) $10\frac{26}{55}$

Exercise 2

1) $1\frac{13}{20}$ 2) $1\frac{7}{20}$ 3) $1\frac{1}{56}$ 4) $1\frac{17}{24}$ 5) $\frac{7}{20}$ 6) $\frac{17}{30}$ 7) $\frac{17}{42}$ 8) $\frac{7}{45}$ 9) $2\frac{5}{26}$ 10) $3\frac{3}{44}$ 11) $3\frac{23}{72}$ 12) $1\frac{15}{26}$

Exercise 3

1) $\frac{31}{8}$ 3.88   2) $\frac{19}{4}$ 4.75   3) $\frac{28}{5}$ 5.6   4) $\frac{55}{8}$ 6.88   5) $\frac{49}{10}$ 4.9   6) $\frac{111}{13}$ 8.54   7) $\frac{80}{11}$ 7.27   8) $\frac{123}{19}$ 6.47
9) $\frac{59}{11}$ 5.36   10) $\frac{110}{17}$ 6.47   11) $\frac{214}{21}$ 10.19   12) $\frac{117}{19}$ 6.16

Exercise 4

1) 1.875   2) 3.75   3) 9.7   4) 6.875   5) 9.175   6) 12.32   7) 14.4375   8) 22.28   9) 16.14   10) 15.3125
11) 28.03125   12) 19.21875

Changing fractions into decimals   Page 85

Exercise

1) 0.111   2) 0.583   3) 0.273   4) 0.091   5) 0.143   6) 0.294   7) 0.615   8) 0.444   9) 0.316   10) 0.348
11) 0.643   12) 0.385   13) 0.217   14) 0.476   15) 0.412   16) 0.364

Estimating   Page 86

Since all the answers are estimates, yours should be close to these.

Exercise 1

1) 8100   2) 1200   3) 60   4) 1500   5) 4000   6) 50,000   7) 20,000   8) 8000   9) 5600   10) 18,000
11) 27,000   12) 80,000

Exercise 2

1) 12   2) 10   3) 10   4) 10   5) 10   6) 10   7) 10   8) 10   9) 10   10) 30   11) 40   12) 20   13) 10
14) 20   15) 15   16) 7

Mental arithmetic   Page 87

Exercise 1

1) 85   2) 70   3) 75   4) 82   5) 85   6) 159   7) 14   8) 33   9) 27   10) 54   11) 27   12) 36

Exercise 2

1) £12   2) £13   3) £17   4) £11   5) £12   6) £12   7) £16   8) £7   9) £16   10) £15

Exercise 3

1) £25.95   2) £32.93   3) £15.97   4) £43.90   5) £26.96   6) £35.95

Recap test 5   Page 88

1) a) 35.96   b) 108.038   2) a) 17.85   b) 3.98   3) a) 96.15   b) 72.36   4) a) 2.06   b) 3.66   5) a) 73p
b) £1.27   6) £12.83 with 2p remaining   7) a) 11.4m   b) 1.05L   8) £1.15   9) £2.45   10) £1.44
11) a) $3\frac{31}{35}$ b) 8.60   12) 0.444   13) 1.429   14) a) 1500   b) 60,000   15) a) 12   b) 20   16) £16
17) a) 56   b) 149   c) 86   d) 162   e) 24   f) 24   g) 36   h) 52   18) £23.95

Imperial measure - Length   Page 89

Exercise 1

1) a) 4'1"   b) 6'1"   c) 7'8"   2) a) 1yd 2ft 3in   b) 2yd 1ft   c) 2yd 2ft 7in   3) a) 48in   b) 72in
c) 60in   d) 15in   e) 53in   f) 223in   4) a) 21 feet   b) 32 feet   c) 48 feet

Exercise 2

1) a) 15ft 3in   b) 5yd 2ft 1in   c) 5yd 4in   2) a) 4ft or 1yd 1ft   b) 1yd 2ft or 5ft   c) 1ft 1in   d) 1ft 10in
e) 2ft 8in

Exercise 3

1) 22.9cm   2) 127cm   3) 21.9yd   4) 45.7 metres   5) 7.9m   6) 23ft   7) 4.8km   8) 12.5miles   9) 175.3cm
10) 4.6ft   11) 7.2km   12) 109.4yd

Imperial measure - Capacity   Page 91

Exercise 1

1) a) 1pt 17fl oz   b) 4pt 16fl oz   c) 5pt 3fl oz   2)   a) 100fl oz   b) 74fl oz   c) 150fl oz   d) 111fl oz
e) 5fl oz   f) 280fl oz   3) a)   2gall 4pt   b) 10gall 2pt   c) 12gall   4) a) 52 pints   b) 38 pints   c) 30 pints

Exercise 2

1) a) 14pt 2fl oz   b) 12pt 6fl oz   c) 6gall 3pt   d) 18gall   2) a) 4pt 5fl oz   b) 3pt 7fl oz   c) 7pt 11fl oz
d) 1gall 5pt   e) 5galls 2pt

Exercise 3

1) 63.7L   2) 104.7L   3) 6.8L   4) 19.9L   5) 24.6pts   6) 75.7pts   7) 3.7galls   8) 7.9galls
9) 10 galls is 45.5L   10) 22.8L

Imperial measure - Weight   Page 93

Exercise 1

1) a) 2lb 6oz   b) 4lb 4oz   c) 6lb 1oz   2) a) 32oz   b) 56oz   c) 37oz   d) 20oz   e) 70oz   f) 151oz
3) a) 1st 13lbs   b) 5st 3lbs   c) 10st   4) a) 126lbs   b) 63lbs   c) 190lbs   d) 63lbs

Exercise 2

1) a) 13lbs 6ozs   b) 6lbs 12ozs   c) 19st 6lbs   d) 27st 9lbs   2) a) 3lbs 4ozs   b) 4lbs 2ozs   c) 3lbs 11ozs
d) 5st 4lbs   e) 2st 11lb

Exercise 3

1) 3.8ozs   2) 56g   3) 5kg   4) 1816g   5) 706g   6) 3.4kg   7) 8.6kg   8) 15.4lbs   9) 27.5lbs   10) 490g
11) 7.1ozs   12) 63.6kg   13) 88.2kg   14) 16st 7lb

Roman numerals   Page 95

Exercise 1

i) 21   ii) 7   iii) 16   iv) 36   v) 65   vi) 117   vii) 127   viii) 168   ix) 366   x) 527   xi) 615   xii) 765
xiii) 1300   xiv) 1615

Exercise 2

i) 90   ii) 190   iii) 490   iv) 990   v) 1990   vi) 1903   vii) 1950   viii) 45   ix) 900   x) 405   xi) 909   xii) 995

Exercise 3

1643   1687   1701   1737   1754   1806   1863   1884   1900   1927   1943   1969   1984   1995

Probability   Page 96

Exercise 1

1) $\frac{1}{6}$ 2) $\frac{1}{13}$ 3) $\frac{4}{7}$ 4) $\frac{1}{18}$ 5) $\frac{1}{2}$ 6) a) $\frac{1}{6}$ b) $\frac{5}{6}$ c) $\frac{1}{2}$ 7) a) $\frac{4}{9}$ b) $\frac{1}{3}$ c) $\frac{2}{9}$ 8) a) $\frac{3}{100}$ b) 25

Exercise 2

Solutions could be e, d, b, c, f, a or e, d, c, b, f, a etc

Recap test 6   Page 98

1) 4'9"   2) 3yd 1ft 6in   3) 96in   4) 3yd 2ft 4in   5) 1'6"   6) a) 66.04cm   b) 11.81in
7) 2 pints 13fl oz   8) 3gall 1pt   9) 5pt 7fl oz   10) 2gall 6pt   11) a) 27 litres   b) 8gall   12) 3lb 9oz
13) 49lb   14) 2 stones 5 pounds   15) a) 15.4lb   b) 13.64kg   16) a) 17   b) 40   c) 160   d) 1111
17) a) LXXIX   b) CLVI   c) CDLIII   d) MCMXLI   18) a) $\frac{7}{10}$ b) $\frac{3}{10}$ c) $\frac{1}{10}$

The Test   Page 99

1) a) 50   b) 80   c) 150   d) 860   e) 1460   2) 410   3) a) 10×50 b) 12×47 or $47 \times 12 = 564$ 4) 55
5) 2348   6) 175   7) six hundred   8) 8154   9) 0.375   10) 74r15   11) $\frac{1}{5}$, 0.23, 25%   12) 420,000

113

13) 60p 14) 3600 15) 90% 16) a) $\frac{8}{17}$ b) $\frac{6}{17}$ c) $\frac{3}{17}$ 17) £47 18) 27 19) a) 160 b) 127,000
c) 870 20) $\frac{2}{3}$ 21) 10,000 22) $1\frac{1}{2}$ 23) 40r5 24) $5\frac{1}{4}$ 25) 6.35 26) $1\frac{5}{8}$ 27) 7248 28) $\frac{5}{8}$
29) a) 10.4 b) 3.7 c) 268.0 30) $1\frac{1}{2}$ 31) The second stall 32) 6 33) £420 and £210
34) 12 and 18 35) a) 75g, 225ml, 90g, 9 eggs, 255g b) 187.5g, 562.5ml, 225g, 22.5 eggs, 637.5g
36) 0.14 37) £5,200 38) 6.9 39) a) 30mins b) 1hr 40mins c) yes 2hrs 35mins needed
40) 0.651 41) a) 31, 36 b) 17, 12 42) 7.48 43) 89.6km 44) 3.59 45) 44sq m
46) £1.14 and 1p left over 47) Bill 48) £85 49) a) unlikely b) unlikely c) even chance d) likely
50) $\frac{11}{20}$ 51) $\frac{1}{6}$ 52) 0.37 53) 11.5 54) 16 55) $1600 \div 40 = 40$ 56) 27.816 57) 248 58) 106°C
59) a) 15% b) 62.5% c) 48% 60) 51.3% 61) $\frac{2}{5}$, 40% 62) 4,300g 63) £12.40 64) 40cl 65) £32.38
66) a) 2°C b) –11°C 67) 8cm 68) 12°C 69) £8 + £4 + £7 + £5 – 4p 70) 100 71) a) $1\frac{1}{12}$ b) $\frac{9}{14}$
c) $2\frac{39}{40}$ 72) $84 - 25 = 59$ or LIX 73) a) 0.625 b) 0.05 c) 3.25 74) £212.40 75) 7 76) CDLVII
77) 490 : 210 78) £160 79) 21 stones 3 pounds 80) 2,571,400 81) 30% 82) 8, 4, 2 83) 8'1"
84) $1\frac{7}{8}$ L 85) 7hrs 22mins 86) 9" 87) 0.286 88) 10 : 35 89) 0-no chance, 0.1-very unlikely,
0.3-unlikely, 0.5-even, 0.7-likely, 0.9-very likely, 1.0-certain 90) a) 15 b) $20 \div 7 = 2.86$ no
91) 12°C 92) £31.25 93) 100 94) $5\frac{5}{51}$ 95) 27sq m 96) 1080cc 97) a) 160,000 b) 160 litres
98) a) 30km b) 120km c) 15km 99) 60 100) a) $119\frac{7}{16}$ sq m b) 220g 101) 35mph 102) a) $\frac{2}{5}$
b) $\frac{1}{3}$ c) $\frac{11}{15}$ 103) 42.5mpg 104) a) 15 b) 13 c) 195 tiles; 20 packs

Proof of the rule for dividing by a fraction

Let the two fractions be called $\frac{a}{b}$ and $\frac{c}{d}$

We want to find

$$\frac{a}{b} \div \frac{c}{d}$$

$$= \left(\frac{a}{b} \times \frac{d}{c}\right) \div \left(\frac{c}{d} \times \frac{d}{c}\right)$$

Here I have multiplied both parts by the same number. This will give the same answer. (Think of $6 \div 2 = 3$
also $6 \times 4 \div 2 \times 4$
$= 24 \div 8 = 3$)

$$= \left(\frac{a}{b} \times \frac{d}{c}\right) \div \left(\frac{c \times d}{d \times c}\right)$$

Here $c \times d$ and $d \times c$ are equal (think of 2×6 and 6×2)

so $\frac{c \times d}{d \times c} = 1$

$$= \left(\frac{a}{b} \times \frac{d}{c}\right) \div 1$$

$$= \quad \frac{a}{b} \times \frac{d}{c}$$

When we divide by 1, the value remains the same. (think of $7 \div 1 = 7$)

Now compare this with the original problem

i.e. $\frac{a}{b} \div \frac{c}{d} = \frac{a}{b} \times \frac{d}{c}$

So to do a problem where we have to divide by a fraction, we must invert the second fraction then multiply the two fractions together.

Index